Internal Auditing
in Plain English

A Simple Guide to Super Effective ISO Audits

Other Paton Professional Books by Craig Cochran

- *ISO 9001:2015 in Plain English*
- *Becoming a Customer-Focused Organization*
- *The Continual Improvement Process*
- *Customer Satisfaction: Tools, Techniques, and Formulas for Success*
- *Internal Auditing in Plain English (Coming Soon)*
- *Problem Solving in Plain English*
- *The 7 Lessons: Management Tools for Success*

Order these and other titles online at *www.patonprofessional.com.*

Internal Auditing
in Plain English

A Simple Guide to Super Effective ISO Audits

Craig Cochran

Chico, California

Most Paton Professional books are available at quantity discounts when purchased in bulk. For more information, contact:

Paton Professional
PO Box 44
Chico, CA 95927-0044
Telephone: (530) 342-5480
Email: *books@patonprofessional.com*
Web: *www.patonprofessional.com*

ISBN: 978-1-932828-16-0

Staff
Publisher: Scott M. Paton
Editor: Laura Smith
Book design: Anita Jovanovic
Cover design: Miguel Kilantang

To Muriel, a model of patience and love

Contents

Introduction

I first began auditing in the late 1980s, right around the time the first edition of ISO 9001 was published. This timing proved very fortunate. As ISO 9001 evolved, so did my auditing skills. After a few years, I realized that I could walk into almost any organization and perform a solid audit. I also realized that audits are never boring. Every single audit was a little different from the others, and I learned something new every time I performed one.

Audits offer limitless opportunities for learning. If you are someone who craves new knowledge and the opportunity to grow, auditing will never let you down. Now, after three decades of auditing, I still learn something new on every audit I perform.

I've also realized over the years that good auditors often make long-term friendships with the people they audit. It sounds a little odd, doesn't it? After all, audits are an examination of sorts. Why would you make friends with your examiner? The reason is that an audit isn't really an examination; it's a partnership for improvement. The auditor is playing on the same team as the auditee. A good auditor isn't trying to uncover bombshells or get anybody in trouble. The role of the auditor is to work with the auditee to show where an organization is meeting requirements and to help the auditee improve. If that's not a good basis for friendship, I don't know what is.

Part of the journey toward becoming an auditor is observing many other people develop as auditors. These observations can be distilled down to one important realization: Anybody can do it. That's right, anybody can become a skilled and effective auditor. The only prerequisite is the desire to do it and the willingness to learn. Sure, there are certain personal attributes that are especially helpful, but they're just bonuses.

Many people reading these words were probably "volun-told" to become auditors. The company needed auditors, and someone put your name on the list. Despite that sinking feeling in your stomach, fear not. You will be successful as an auditor if you can convince yourself that the positives outweigh the negatives, and you really *do* want to try. A few ounces of desire can convert to tons of success over your auditing career.

One of the most surprising things about auditing is the amount of *fun* it generates. Auditing is a lot of fun. Remember the fun you had participating in scavenger hunts? This is quite like auditing. You will observe audit trails that represent huge improvement opportunities for the organization. To fully reveal the truth, you will need to follow that audit trail and interpret the evidence. Digging to the bottom of situations is fun and rewarding. You might discover knowledge that nobody else in the organization has. Those of you who wanted to be explorers or detectives when you grew up... now's your chance! Every audit is full of discoveries and epiphanies, and the process of uncovering them can only be described as fun.

Welcome to the wonderful world of auditing. You are embarking on a positive and satisfying journey that will have a significant, positive effect on the organizations you audit.

I hope this book will be an essential partner along the way.

Chapter 1

Principles of Internal Auditing

P rinciples are an excellent way to begin our exploration of internal auditing. After all, they're the ideas that form the foundation of any successful audit program. Many of these principles may seem like common sense, but I've come to understand that common sense is indeed not very common. Even smart and experienced auditors sometimes forget these principles. That's why we should build the audit program around these ideas and continually reinforce them. Let's examine each one and discuss what it means.

FOCUS ON PROCESSES, NOT PEOPLE

A great deal of evidence gathered during the audit comes from people. That's because organizations are made up of people. People analyze information, make decisions, and create products. Although they are a primary source of evidence, people aren't the focus of the audit. Audits should focus on processes, methods, and procedures. People are the conduit through which we learn about processes.

When there are audit nonconformities (and trust me, there will be), we make changes to our processes, not our people. A focus on people leads to corrective actions such as verbal reprimands, written warnings, and dismissals. These corrective actions don't change the way work is done. We might have changed the *people*, but the same flawed *methods* will be in place. Effective audits focus on the *process*. The resulting corrective actions aim to improve that process. The only way to make improvements is by changing the way work is being done.

DON'T STRIVE TO FIND NONCONFORMITIES

This principle probably sounds very strange, given the way some auditors conduct themselves. Auditors should try to find evidence that the organization *is* meeting its requirements. However, it's not uncommon that nonconformities will be observed. Nonconformities or not, the auditor's attitude is one of someone performing an improvement activity in partnership with the auditee. An audit is not a "gotcha" exercise. A good auditor examines a reasonable sample of evidence and draws resulting conclusions. No need to keep digging and digging until nonconformities are found. As far as I know, no auditor has ever been paid by the number of nonconformities he or she finds.

One of the most profound outcomes of an audit are the best practices it reveals, especially in a mature management system. Effective audits identify isolated pockets of excellence that are unknown to the wider organization. In this way, the audit becomes almost like a benchmarking exercise, with parts of the organization learning from other parts. An effective auditor begins each audit in a "learning" state of mind. He or she expects to find best practices and positives to learn from. This makes the auditor especially receptive to the good things the organization is doing.

Auditors are naturally curious and persistent, so it's hard to suppress the satisfaction you might feel when you uncover a nonconformity. There is a visceral thrill that an auditor feels when he or she identifies a problem that can affect the success of the organization. Nevertheless, the effective auditor always conducts himself or herself in a professional manner. No cheering, high-fives, or shouts of ecstasy when you find a nonconformity, please.

KEEP YOURSELF UNBIASED AND IMPARTIAL

In a word, effective auditors are fair. They simply examine evidence and draw factual conclusions. This can be especially challenging for internal auditors because you usually know most of the people you're auditing. You know the people who are smart, silly, careless, and downright reckless. In fact, there are probably people you like and people who (gasp!) you don't like. The effective auditor has to lock away all these opinions during the audit and approach the audit with a fresh set of eyes and an open mind. Just because you feel certain that the guys in the warehouse are a bunch of idiots, you must treat them in the same way you do everybody else. You don't dig deeper and try harder to find nonconformities because of your personal opinions. When an auditor has especially strong feelings about certain functions—either good or bad—he or she must realize there is no way to remain unbiased. In these cases, auditors should work with the lead auditor to find someone else who can audit the function impartially. Fairness is the consistent thread that runs through every effective audit.

Independence is another aspect of being impartial. This refers to being organizationally separate from the function that you audit. You certainly don't audit your own work and you avoid auditing your department. It's best not to audit any area where you have an existing reporting relationship. No matter how hard you try to be unbiased, you're tied to the function, and you're likely to be influenced by the relationship.

MAINTAIN CONFIDENTIALITY

The results of the audit don't belong to you. They belong to the entity requesting the audit, known as the "audit client." This is usually top management. The audit results go to top management, and they are also shared (at least verbally) with the auditee, but that is as far as they go. The audit client gets to decide who else will hear the audit results. It's your responsibility as an auditor to maintain confidentiality over the results. Audit "war stories" make interesting conversation, but they should never stray into the territory of talking about the weaknesses of an organization. Maintaining confidentiality is a professional courtesy, of course, but it's also a matter of self-preservation. Auditors who betray confidentiality won't be invited back.

BASE THE AUDIT ON REQUIREMENTS AND EVIDENCE

Two basic principles lie at the heart of auditing:
- An understanding of relevant requirements
- A search for evidence that meets requirements

The factual approach of requirements and evidence keeps the audit purely objective. The auditor's opinion of what *should* be done has no relevance. What matters is what the organization has committed to, and whether it's meeting those commitments. Auditors certainly have opinions, and most have valuable experience in the industries they audit. However, an audit is not a consulting visit. It's a friendly evaluation aimed at driving improvements. When audits stray from a strict focus on requirements and evidence, they become fuzzy and subjective—exactly what you don't want. We'll discuss requirements and evidence in detail later in the book.

BE PROFESSIONAL

Effective auditors are consummate professionals. This doesn't mean they're stiff unblinking robots who refuse to crack a smile. It simply means they're good communicators, well-prepared, smartly attired, and cordial. When someone is going through the trouble of being audited, they want to know the auditor is a pro. This provides credibility of the audit process and lets the participants know it won't be a waste of time. Professionalism doesn't necessarily rely on years of experience, either. I've seen novice auditors who were exceptionally professional and veteran auditors who were less professional than a circus clown. It all goes back to preparation. If you prepare for the audit and arrive ready to produce excellent results, you will be truly professional.

BEYOND BASIC PRINCIPLES

It's helpful for auditors to think about the audit as a series of friendly conversations. The auditor chats with employees about their methods, tools, materials, and products. The information revealed during the conversations is compared to the organization's requirements, and the auditor determines whether the organization is meeting its commitments. In either case, the determination isn't a secret.

If an organization is meeting requirements, or even going above and beyond requirements, the auditor will congratulate the employees who make that happen. If it's not meeting commitments, the auditor confirms his or her understanding of the requirements and the evidence. We don't assume anything. A good auditor verifies everything he or she sees and hears because it's very easy to misinterpret information during an audit. The process of gathering evidence and determining conformity is conducted like a conversation among partners. As an auditor, that's exactly what you are: a partner in the organization's improvement process.

Top management must be involved in the audit process. They will certainly be audited, and they may even act as auditors themselves. Having top management clearly involved in auditing gives the process credibility. This credibility is like a passport to all corners of the organization. When you are supported by top management, auditees will cooperate and provide you with whatever you need. Following the principles in this chapter will enable you to get top management support and maintain the attention of the entire organization. After all, you're there to help the organization. Yes, I know the old joke, "We're auditors and we're here to help you." When you audit a management system it's true. Believe it, and carry the rest of these principles with you wherever you audit.

BENEFITS OF AUDITING

By now, you might be thinking, "Auditing sounds like a lot of trouble. Why bother?" The reason is that it delivers a lot of value to the organization. Managers benefit from learning about potential problems and auditors grow in experience and exposure. Here's a brief list of the benefits you can expect to receive from a well-developed internal audit program.

Managers will:

- Discover what's going on within the organization, which allows for more objective decision making.
- Learn of potential problems before they explode into issues that pose significant risk to the organization.
- Identify when failures occur, enabling the containment of these problems and initiation of corrective action.
- Identify where resources should be directed.
- Determine how effective their training efforts are.

- Learn which processes and personnel are particularly effective, which can trigger recognition.

For their part, internal auditors will:
- Gain exposure to other parts of the organization, which broadens their experience.
- Be exposed to best practices they can implement in their own departments.
- Learn how they contribute to the organization's success, which increases motivation and employee retention.
- Expand the organization's competency and knowledge base through their experience.

Internal auditing is the classic win-win formula. Everybody who takes part in it will gain something. But before we reap the benefits of an effective audit process, top management must establish an audit program. That's the topic of our next chapter.

FREQUENTLY ASKED QUESTIONS

Our quality director has suggested that each auditor needs to write at least three nonconformities during each audit. Does this make sense?

No. The purpose of auditors is not to write nonconformities, but to seek evidence that we're meeting our commitments. Sometimes this results in nonconformities and sometimes it doesn't.

My management is encouraging the audit team to write nonconformities against best practices. In other words, things that we know are wrong, but for which there are no known requirements. Can we do this?

No. Nonconformities are always written against solid requirements. Standards such as "best practice," "industry standard," and "world-class methods" are subjective and meaningless.

Our employees are terrified of auditing. What can we do to remove their anxiety?

Educate them! Make sure they understand that audits focus on processes and procedures, not on people. Nobody will get in trouble as a result of audits. Participating on an audit team is a terrific opportunity for employees to demonstrate their knowledge and skills, which are likely to be impressive.

Chapter 2

Establishing the Audit Program

As with everything else in an organization, the internal audit program starts with top management. Auditing is meaningless without the full support and sponsorship of leadership. Does that mean that top managers will be audit experts? Hardly. It's rare that top management knows very much at all about auditing. Top management establishes the audit program through three key actions:

- Select someone to lead audit program.
- Communicate the audit program to the organization.
- Ensure resources for the audit program.

Top management has other responsibilities, especially related to analyzing trends in audit results and reviewing corrective actions, but we'll address those later. The three tasks mentioned above specifically relate to getting the internal audit program started. Let's discuss each of these tasks.

SELECT SOMEONE TO LEAD THE AUDIT PROGRAM

Top management is the starting point, but the audit manager takes the ball and runs with it. The term "audit manager" is arbitrary. The person leading the internal audit program could be called the audit manager, audit director, quality manager, lead auditor, or any number of other titles. The key is not what title he or she has, but what *competencies* he or she has. The most critical competencies are shown below:

- *Communication.* Communication is the oil that flows through the auditing engine. The audit manager must be equally adept at both written and verbal communication. He or she must have the experience to prepare carefully crafted communications that are direct and diplomatic. He or she must also be able to evaluate other auditor's communication skills and provide feedback. Communication is possibly the single most important competency.

- *Audit principles.* These are the foundational ideas on which effective audit programs are based. They include traits such as a focus on processes, not striving to find nonconformities, keeping yourself unbiased, maintaining confidentiality, basing the audit on requirements and evidence, and being professional. These concepts were described in detail in the previous chapter.

- *Audit techniques and procedures.* This topic comprises the practicalities of how an audit happens. A significant portion of this book is dedicated to audit techniques. These include audit planning, interviewing, evidence gathering, and writing nonconformities. Audit techniques and procedures are often learned through a lead auditor course, but there are many other ways to learn them. The audit manager should be well versed in the full range of audit techniques.

- *Standard requirements.* Most management systems are based on an international standard of some sort. The most common standard is ISO 9001 but there are many others. Thankfully, audit techniques generally remain the same regardless of the standard being used. One of the challenges of auditing is that you are using two different sets of criteria for the audit: the international standard and the company's documentation. In theory, the company's documentation will be written to conform with the international standard adopted by the organization, but this connection is sometimes tenuous. Auditors must keep their eyes on both sets of criteria.

- *Company documentation.* This category encompasses all the various documents written by the organization. These include policies, procedures, work instructions, flowchart specifications, and many other information sources. The audit manager certainly doesn't need to commit these to memory, but he or she should be aware of their existence and know which documents apply to which departments. Company documentation comprises the single most important source of requirements during an audit, as they're generated by the company and presumably have more relevance.

- *Diplomacy.* This is the ability to communicate important messages without making people angry. Because auditing often produces nonconformities and opportunities for improvement, diplomacy must always be applied. Most people don't mind hearing how they can improve if the message is delivered in a sensitive and balanced to way. Diplomacy, like all competencies, can be learned, but it also tends to be an essential personality trait.

COMMUNICATE THE AUDIT PROGRAM TO THE ORGANIZATION

Once top managers have selected a competent person to lead the audit program, they must let the organization know what's coming. The communication doesn't need to be grandiose, just a simple heads-up that the organization will begin doing internal audits of its processes. The communication will track very closely to the audit principles we discussed in chapter 1, with a few extra topics thrown in. Here is a basic outline of what top management should tell everybody:

- *Audits will help us improve.* This is the overarching message: The purpose of doing these audits is to help us get better. We will not only look for flaws in our processes, but also for strengths in our processes that should become the new standard. Our internal audits will be a truly balanced snap shot of how our processes are functioning.
- *Internal audit will be led by [insert name here].* This is where you identify the audit manager and say a few words about why he or she is ideally suited to the role. Experience with quality assurance, auditing, or improvement efforts are often cited. The point is to give everyone confidence in the person taking the lead. This person usually has other roles, so he or she may already be well known to the organization.
- *Audits aren't intended to get anybody in trouble.* Yes, our auditors will speak to a wide range of personnel throughout the organization. The focus of

the audit will be on our processes, though. If there are nonconformities detected during internal audits, they will typically be treated as flaws of our processes and procedures, not flaws of people.

- *Everybody is expected to cooperate.* When you see your department scheduled for an audit, make time for it. Tell your employees what to expect and make sure they cooperate. There's nothing scary about an audit. Just treat it like a friendly conversation and don't try to hide anything.

- *Audits will be scheduled in advance.* There will be no surprise audits. You'll know when they will happen and you'll know the topics of the audit. In this way, the audit will be a cooperative improvement event.

- *Any nonconformities will be handled through corrective action.* If we find problems, we will fix the processes. The objective is to make our work more effective and more efficient. Please note that corrective action is not the same as disciplinary action. Our focus will always be on our processes and procedures.

- *If anybody is interested in auditing, please contact your supervisor.* This final message is optional. The organization may have already hand-selected the employees it wants to serve as internal auditors. It's common to be very familiar with the employees who are perceptive, detailed, and industrious. If you'd like a pool of applicants, however, this is a good time to ask for them.

You will certainly need to fine-tune these messages depending on your unique circumstances. The communication can be provided through a variety of means, though in-person is preferable. When employees see top management talking about internal audits online and in-person, the importance is indisputable. It also provides an opportunity for questions and answers. Top management should plan on having the audit manager present to help answer any questions. An all-hands meeting, town hall, or quarterly review are great forums that already take place in many organizations, and these can be adapted very effectively to talk about internal auditing. No matter what you do, don't make the mistake of beginning an internal audit process without letting everybody know what's happening.

ENSURE RESOURCES FOR THE AUDIT PROGRAM

Like any organizational process, internal audits require resources to be successful. The resources are an investment in your organization's success and could be correctly categorized as a preventive cost. Internal audits will identify problems and potential problems before they blossom into serious threats. The preventive cost of auditing is significantly less than the costs of dealing with problems once they reach customers. Here are the most typical resources required for a successful internal audit program.

Internal auditors

The single biggest cost of doing internal audits is the time it takes to complete them. Auditors put their regular jobs on hold briefly while they audit. More frequent audits of shorter duration are more effective because they're less disruptive and easier for the organization to digest. Half-day audits, spread throughout the year, seem to work very well. This strategy enables auditors to spend at least part of the audit day on their regular jobs. At the beginning of an audit effort, it's also recommended that auditors work in pairs. This provides a valuable opportunity for others to learn from each other and leverage each other's strengths.

Imagine a hypothetical organization with ten departments or processes. We can begin to get a rough idea of how much auditing time might be necessary. Figure 2.1 illustrates the investment.

In this hypothetical organization, it would require 10 work days to perform internal audits over the course of a year. As auditors become more experienced, this time might decrease. For instance, auditors could work independently instead of in pairs and the planning and reporting activities could be expedited. Internal auditing is still a significant investment, no matter how you cut it. The benefit you get from this is highly dependent on the time you put into it.

The size of your organization will dictate how many internal auditors you need. Figure 2.2 illustrates some basic guidelines gleaned from many years of coaching and managing internal audit processes.

Figure 2.1	Audit time by process		
Process	Duration of audit	Number of auditors	Person days
1. Top management	0.5	2	1
2. Sales/ customer service	0.5	2	1
3. Purchasing	0.5	2	1
4. Receiving/ shipping	0.5	2	1
5. Production	0.5	2	1
6. Inspection	0.5	2	1
7. Maintenance	0.5	2	1
8. Warehouse	0.5	2	1
9. Documentation	0.5	2	1
10. Improvement	0.5	2	1
TOTAL	5 days	2 auditors	10 person days

Choosing the right number of auditors is a balancing act. If you have too few, your auditors will burn out and will hate doing it. If you have too many, they won't gain sufficient experience and won't be confident about their skills. The recommended numbers above take both points into consideration, but they are by no means cast in stone. Every organization should experiment with and see what works best for them.

Auditor training

Once you've selected auditors, they must be trained. This training typically requires at least two days, and it's recommended that the training be provided by an external organization with experience in adult learners. After you have an established audit program, you could provide the training in-

Figure 2.2	Number of auditors by number of employees
Total employees in organization	Auditors desired
2 to 10 employees	2 auditors
11 to 15 employees	3 auditors
15 to 20 employees	4 auditors
21 to 30 employees	5 auditors
31 to 50 employees	6 auditors
51 to 100 employees	8 auditors
101 to 200 employees	15 auditors
201 to 300 employees	20 auditors
300+ employees	20–25 auditors

ternally, but starting out with an external training provider will prove more effective. If you have four or more employees to be trained at the same time, it's usually cost effective to bring the training to your organization. In this way, the examples and exercises can be tailored to your unique environment.

It's recommended that at least one employee receive lead auditor training. This is typically a five-day training course that takes place at an offsite location. Lead auditor courses address auditing from every angle and stress the management of the overall audit program. The audit manager would be an obvious candidate for this type of training, if he or she hasn't already received it.

Problem solving training

The next type of training is aimed the people who manage the processes being audited. Nonconformities resulting from an audit will generate corrective actions. These corrective actions might include meaningful process improvements or they may amount to fancy words that mean nothing. It all depends on how well people understand what corrective action is all about.

Your managers and key personnel will most likely need training on how to take effective corrective action. This training could go by many different names: problem solving, root cause analysis, corrective action, process improvement. Regardless of the name, the consistent theme is that it will provide a systematic and disciplined way to taking corrective action on nonconformities. Problem-solving training is typically provided in one- or two-day formats, though there are courses that can run significantly longer.

FREQUENTLY ASKED QUESTIONS

Our top management isn't interested in supporting our internal audit program. I've asked for resources, but the response is "Just go audit." Is this possible?

Not really. Without a strategic approach to auditing that's supported by resources and top management, the program will go nowhere. Try to educate top managers of the benefits of auditing and why it's worth their full support.

One of our administrative people is very enthusiastic about auditing. She's not in the quality department now, but she audited at a previous job. Could she lead our auditing program?

Sure. The word "quality" doesn't need to be in anybody's title to lead the audit program. Enthusiasm, energy, and diplomacy are key personality traits that help someone succeed in this role.

Our top management doesn't want us to make a big announcement about the internal audit program. They want it to be more of a "covert operation." Is this a good idea?

No! There's nothing covert about internal audits. They are a completely open and transparent process to drive improvement. Auditors should be viewed as partners in improvement, not police.

Do we have to identify someone as the "lead auditor"?

No. However, if you are auditing in teams of two or more people, having someone designated as the lead can have logistical value. This decision is completely up to you.

Chapter 3

Writing an Internal Audit Procedure

The internal audit procedure is the guiding document of your audit process. It describes in concise detail all of the audit program phases, including scheduling, planning, execution, reporting, corrective action, and close out.

Do everybody a favor and keep the procedure short and sweet by addressing the details in clear and practical terms. There's no reason to reinvent the wheel with your internal audit procedure. Borrow the concepts from other audit procedures and use the ones that seem the most effective. The topics below are most often addressed in an internal audit procedure:

- *Scope of the audit program.* Here you will describe exactly what parts of the organization are covered by the internal audit program. You might also say if your management system is based on an international standard of some sort.

- *Scheduling.* Describe how the organization is notified of upcoming audits. Generally, this is published in advance and made publically available. Internal audits aren't a surprise. You might also say what would prompt a revision in the audit schedule, such as too many nonconformities or increased risk. It's also typical to designate responsibility for maintaining the audit schedule.

- *Planning.* The timing of individual audits is usually controlled through written plans, which show hour by hour exactly what will be examined.

The audit procedures will often designate advance planning and to whom it's communicated. Responsibility for developing the audit plan must also be established.

- *Auditor preparation.* To be effective, auditors must spend time preparing for the audit. This might include reading auditee procedures, reviewing the standard on which the system is based, understanding the processes and products of the auditee, researching the technology, looking at past nonconformities, and reviewing customer complaints. The audit procedure might also require the development of a written checklist prior to the audit.

- *Opening meeting.* The audit procedure will usually require a brief opening meeting that must take place prior to any actual auditing. During this opening meeting the lead auditor will go over the audit plan and make any necessary changes.

- *Evidence gathering.* Evidence is gathered by sampling information from employee interviews, records, observation of processes, and other means. If certain tools should be used during evidence gathering, such as forms or checklists, they should be identified in the audit procedure.

- *Recording of findings.* Audit findings can be both positive and negative. Many audit procedures will stipulate very specific ways to document these findings. Nonconformities are generally written up in a two-part format: requirement and evidence. This is an area where you want the audit procedure to drive consistency.

- *Closing meeting.* The closing meeting is where the audit findings are shared with the auditee. The audit procedures will usually discuss what should be communicated during the closing meeting and who should participate in it.

- *Audit reporting.* Internal audits usually generate reports. The audit procedures will discuss what should be included in this report, who should write it, and how quickly it should be provided to the client. The client is the entity requesting the audit, and this is sometimes different from the auditee.

- *Corrective action on nonconformities.* The audit procedure should clearly state how audit nonconformities will be handled. Audit nonconformities are nearly always handled through corrective action. The audit procedures will designate whose responsibility it is to generate a corrective action. It will also usually reference the corrective action procedure.

- *Follow-up on corrective action.* The audit procedure will usually designate who will follow up on corrective actions. It may also designate time frame required for the follow-up, but this might be dictated by the complexity of the issue in the corrective action.
- *Linkage to management review.* Top management reviews a variety of information about the management system during a forum called management review. The audit procedure will usually mention that audit results will be part of the management review agenda and it may also say whose responsibility is to present these results.

The internal audit process is a process just like any other within the organization. As such, it's also subject to being audited. This means we're expected to follow our internal audit procedure. The internal audit procedure is also subject to change. It should be revised as processes are improved and audit methods evolve. In many ways, the functioning of the internal audit process should serve as a model of excellence for all other processes within the organization.

FREQUENTLY ASKED QUESTIONS

Can our internal audit procedure be a flowchart?
Sure! That would be a simple and intuitive way to describe a process.

Does everybody in our company need to read our internal audit procedure?
No. Only the people directly involved in the process would likely benefit from an in-depth understanding of it.

FREQUENTLY ASKED QUESTIONS

We have created forms for nearly every aspect of auditing, trying to make it as simple as possible. Are we in danger of insulting the intelligence of our auditors?

No. Auditing is something most people do once a month, at the most. They don't audit enough to develop their own tools and forms. Provide as many ready-made resources as possible to make it easy on your auditors.

Chapter 4

Selecting and Training Internal Auditors

Your selection of internal auditors will have a significant effect on the success of your audit program. After all, these people are the living face of your program. Sure, you have someone fulfilling the role of audit manager, but the real magic happens with the team of internal auditors you recruit and train. Don't make the mistake of selecting people whose only qualification is that they have some extra time on their hands. Choose the *right* people who will help develop the audit program and make it a true engine for improvement. What sort of criteria should you use when selecting internal auditors? Here are some attributes to look for:

- *Curiosity.* Good auditors want to know how things work. Everything about a process is fascinating to them: the materials, tasks, equipment, measurements, and products. Good auditors aren't curious about these details because they want to write nonconformities; they're curious because they want to learn. Intellectual curiosity is at the heart of auditing. When auditors are naturally curious, they will automatically ask probing, insightful questions. And they will learn very quickly how effective the process is.

- *Persistence.* This is what I would refer to as "stick-to-it-ness." Auditing can be a very challenging activity, but a good auditor thrives on these challenges and keeps on going. He or she has the strength and determination to get the job done. People who are satisfied with giving a minimal effort don't make good auditors. It's important to note that auditing can be a physically—as well as mentally—challenging activity.

- *Focus.* The ability to keep your thought patterns aligned with the task at hand is an essential trait for good auditors. When you are an internal auditor, distractions abound. Phones ring, emails ding, people come to you with problems and questions. Despite all this, a good auditor politely shoos away distractions and stays focused on the audit. This requires equal parts of diplomacy and resolve. Not only does the auditor have to be focused, but he or she also has to help the auditee stay focused. The same distractions that can sidetrack an auditor will also sidetrack an auditee.

- *Detail orientation.* Auditing is all about details. Yes, truly great auditing involves the recognition of trends, but all trends begin as individual details that somebody must discover. Good auditors pick up on details that other people miss. They use their senses simultaneously: sight, sound, smell, touch. Through these diverse interfaces, they receive and process a wide range of information. Of course, it's always tempting for a detail-oriented person to nitpick. This temptation is countered by reminding oneself that ultimately the internal auditor is seeking conformance, not nonconformance.

- *Strategic thinking.* We expect top managers to think strategically. But, strategic thinking involves looking beyond daily tasks and contemplating long-term, consequential actions an organization could take. Strategic thinking is difficult because the majority of employees are task oriented. They're paid to perform specific activities, not think about what could happen five years from now. A good auditor incorporates strategic thinking into an audit by delving deep into the processes that affect future success. These include:
  ✓ Top management and management review
  ✓ Customer feedback
  ✓ Risk management
  ✓ Corrective action
  ✓ Internal auditing
  ✓ Product realization

Not all processes are created equal, and it's the job of the strategic-minded auditor to recognize the important ones. A strategic auditor can recognize which opportunities and nonconformities pose the biggest risk and highlight them in the audit report.

- *Enthusiasm.* Good auditors are enthusiastic about their missions. They understand the benefits of auditing and believe in the process. They want to audit because it feeds their intellectual curiosity. An auditor's enthusiasm rubs off on everybody else. Little by little, this enthusiasm helps build a culture of continual improvement within the organization.

As you identify candidates to serve as internal auditors, make sure to talk with their supervisors. Discuss auditing and the expected time commitments with the person's supervisor before speaking to the candidate. The supervisor will certainly have questions about what auditing involves, why his or her subordinate was selected, how it could affect the department's workload. Address all these issues and get supervisor support before going any further.

HOW TO SELL THE AUDITING ROLE

Based on the personal attributes listed above, it's obvious that we're seeking some impressive people to serve as internal auditors. The obstacle with impressive people is that they're already busy. As you propose the idea of people serving as internal auditors, one of the first responses you'll hear from these folks is, "Hey, I already have too much to do." Your job is to sell the benefits of serving in this role, and thankfully the benefits are many. We discussed some of these in chapter 1, but here are some selling points in more detail:

- *You will see parts of the organization nobody else gets to see.* Internal auditing is the best on-the-job training exercise imaginable. As an internal auditor, you will have a deeper and broader understanding of the organization than anybody else.
- *Auditing is endlessly fascinating.* This statement comes from someone who has performed auditing for thirty years. You will never get bored auditing. It's an activity that will keep you engaged and challenged, no matter how long you do it.

- *You will learn something new every time you audit.* Best practices pop up all the time during audits. You will discover innovative practices and innovative methods, some of them completely informal and preserved only through verbal communication. As an auditor, you'll be able to expose these methods to the rest of the organization.

- *You will initiate significant improvements.* You will have unparalleled ability to influence change in the organization.

- *You will catch the eye of top management.* Few employees have the visibility of top managers, but as an auditor you will have their undivided attention. You will present the opportunities and nonconformities you uncover directly to top management for their review.

- *Auditing will make you more effective and successful in your regular job.* Your experience as an internal auditor will have an immediate and positive effect on what you do now for the company. How? You will be able to apply best practices and avoid nonconformities.

- *You won't have to audit all the time.* Internal auditing is a periodic activity. The actual time commitment will be a few hours per month. Top management supports your involvement and will make sure that you don't get overwhelmed.

Ultimately, you might have the ability to "volun-tell" someone that they are going to be an internal auditor. If that's the case, good for you, but it's still important to make the benefits clear to new auditors. They will operate much more effectively if they understand what they're getting out of the arrangement.

Try to recruit a wide range of personnel

The ideal audit team consists of diverse personnel from different backgrounds and different parts of the organization. This makes for a team that will challenge itself and examine audit evidence from vastly different perspectives. When you have auditors with a wide range of experiences, your team is better able to understand and audit all processes within the organization. You won't fall into the trap of people trying to audit departments with which they have no familiarity, and you also won't fall victim to group think. Try to get representation across the full spectrum of personnel, including:

- Hourly employees
- Salaried employees
- Production employees (manufacturing or service)
- Front office administrative employees (e.g., purchasing, accounting, human resources)
- Engineering and technical employees

The personal attributes shown in first section of this chapter are the most important selection criteria for internal auditors. If you're able, also strive for diversity of backgrounds, experience, and organizational roles. Your audit team will be stronger and more flexible.

Training for internal auditors

When you have assembled a solid team of candidates, the next obligation is training them. Auditing isn't a process that many people are naturally good at. They need exposure to the full range of auditing tools and techniques, along with opportunities to practice them under supervised conditions. Online training only is seldom effective. Neither will classroom training all by itself. These are the most common training topics for internal auditors:

- *Audit principles.* As you know by now, audit principles are the foundation upon which we build the audit program. They are the important ideas that auditors need to understand and adopt.
- *Standard requirements.* Most management systems are based on an international standard of some sort, such as ISO 9001. The big challenge is that these standards are often hard to understand. They're full of requirements, but the actual meaning of those requirements can be a bit fuzzy. Auditor training needs to cover standard requirements in detail, with an emphasis on practical interpretations.
- *Audit procedure.* The audit procedure is the document that describes how an audit should happen. By the time you conduct auditor training, you will have a written audit procedure, and all your internal auditors need to understand what it says.

- *Preparing for an audit.* You don't just wake up one morning and start doing an audit. There's a significant amount of preparation that must happen even for a short audit. This includes refreshing yourself on the procedures in the department you'll be auditing and developing some preliminary audit trails. It could also include the development of an audit checklist

- *Developing an audit plan.* The audit plan is a simple, concise document that says where you're going to go and what you're going to do during the audit. It should cover times, places, and topics to discuss. Like any multifaceted plan, it takes some training and practice to develop.

- *Interviewing techniques.* At its heart, auditing is nothing more than a friendly conversation. It's a conversation with a very specific objective: to gather evidence that indicates conformity. As such, there are some methods to this conversation that we will label "interview techniques." The better your auditors know interviewing techniques, the smoother the audit will go.

- *Audit requirements.* Audit requirements are the full set of criteria you can use during the audit. They include standard requirements, procedures, policies, work instructions, and contracts the organization adopts. Auditor opinions never constitute requirements.

- *Objective evidence.* This is what you're seeking during the audit. It's the factual, unbiased, and verifiable proof that we either met or didn't meet the audit requirements. Sometimes it's easy to get objective evidence mixed up with subjective evidence.

- *Matching evidence to requirements.* One of the keys to auditing is matching evidence to requirements. It's a relatively simple task once auditors understand the logic and have had some practice with it. Failure to match evidence to requirements means that the auditor is wasting everybody's time.

- *Writing nonconformities.* Writing is a difficult task no matter what the context. Writing audit nonconformities is an especially difficult task because you're balancing detail with brevity; you've got to state the facts, but you can't write a book. Some people believe they're being personally evaluated during an audit, which raises the stakes even higher.

- *Conducting opening and closing meetings.* The bookends of the audit are the opening and closing meetings. Auditors need to understand how to conduct these meetings in a dignified and professional way, yet still retain personal warmth. Closing meetings are especially important because this is where we officially discuss the audit results.
- *Audit reporting.* The written output of the internal audit is what we refer to as audit reporting. The audit report must be clear, concise, and no longer than necessary. It takes some practice to achieve this.
- *The link to corrective action.* There is a direct and critical connection between internal auditing and corrective action. Internal auditors need to understand the corrective action system just as well as they understand auditing.
- *Follow-up on audit findings.* Finally, auditors need to be trained on how to follow up and close out audit findings. This is one of the most neglected phases of the audit process because it takes place well after the audit is completed.

Don't burn out your auditors

It's human nature to use your best resources. If you have a patch of ground that produces great tomatoes, it's tempting to keep planting tomatoes there, year after year. The only problem is that the soil eventually becomes exhausted. This is the case with an internal audit program, too. Experienced and well-trained auditors produce effective results, so they frequently get called on to perform audits. Thus, the organization fails to develop new auditors.

One of the best strategies is to make each auditor's assignment 18 months long. Annually, train a new group of auditors, and then use the remaining six months for the experienced auditors to mentor the new group. Schedule auditors in teams of two, one new auditor and one experienced. That way, the new auditors get the benefit of observing the experienced auditors in action, and the experienced auditors can learn from the new perspectives and unburdened approaches employed by the new auditors.

After a few years of rotating in new groups of auditors, you'll have used a significant chunk of your employees. The benefits of doing this are clear:

- Broad exposure of personnel to other functions in the organizations
- Deeper understanding of the management system and its processes
- Stronger communication and analysis skills because of auditing experience
- Varied perspectives and viewpoints that come from using a wide range of personnel as auditors
- Less likelihood that the audit process will fall victim to group think
- You will have an informal "alumni association" of former auditors who can be called on to perform audits periodically if you get into a pinch

Don't settle for less than the best when you assemble your internal audit team. Sell the program enthusiastically to potential auditor candidates and clearly communicate all the benefits of this important role. Internal auditors with strong personal attributes—combined with effective training—will become engines of improvement.

FREQUENTLY ASKED QUESTIONS

My top management only wants to use hourly employees as auditors because they don't believe the role is important enough for anybody else. Is this correct?

No. For companies interested in making improvements, there are few things as important as internal audits. The richer the mix of auditors the better.

We got a video to teach our personnel how to audit. What do you think of that?

It's not likely to be very effective. Auditing is best taught through an interactive workshop format that allows plenty of practice auditing, role playing, and challenging exercises. This should be followed by performing real audits while under the supervision of an experienced auditor.

FREQUENTLY ASKED QUESTIONS

We've had the same auditors for more than five years. Should we change them out?

Yes! It's great to have dedicated auditors who know the process, but this experience should be spread around the organization. Overused auditors become ineffective and—even worse—negative about auditing.

Do we have to identify someone as the "lead auditor"?

No. If you are auditing in teams of two or more people, having someone designated as the lead can have logistical value, though. This decision is completely up to you.

Do we have to send one or more of our employees to "lead auditor" training?

No. Some organizations see value in the intensive and in-depth lead auditor training experience. It can help auditors, especially ones with responsibility over junior team members, understand their leadership roles. The decision of making lead auditor training a requirement is entirely up to each organization.

Chapter 5

Audit Scheduling

udit scheduling is one of the most essential activities for managing
the overall audit process. It involves dividing up all the various audits
that will take place over an extended timeframe, usually a year, and
showing when they will take place. The output of audit scheduling is an audit
schedule, a document that looks a lot like a calendar in most cases. The audit
schedule is published throughout the organization and revised on a periodic
basis.

The audit schedule drives the entire audit process. It communicates to
auditors when they must audit and what the scope will be. The audit scope
is simply the boundaries of the audit, usually expressed as a process or a department. Here are the two most typical approaches to developing an audit
schedule:

- Several short duration audits (2-4 hours) throughout the year
- One or two large audits that last a day or more.

Deciding which approach to take is a balance of many factors, including
resources, time, and practicality. In general, having one or two audits every
year is easier from an audit management standpoint, especially if travel is
involved. There is still planning, reporting, and follow-up, but it only happens a couple of times a year. With audits of a day or more in duration, the
audit process becomes more of an event that personnel "get ready for." Long
stretches of time can elapse between audits, thus the discipline that drives a
quality management system (QMS) can erode. Less-frequent audits tend to

also limit the organization's experience with auditing, both from an auditor and auditee standpoint.

A more effective approach is having many audits throughout the year. This produces more routine scrutiny of your processes and maintains a higher level of QMS discipline. Another benefit of frequent audits is that it gives your auditors plenty of practice. When auditors only audit once or twice a year, they never become particularly effective or confident. Finally, frequent audits get everybody accustomed to being interviewed and producing evidence. Ultimately it removes the fear of the audit process.

PROS AND CONS OF BOTH APPROACHES

Large, infrequent audits

Pros:
- There is less frequent audit planning.
- There are fewer disruptions to operations.
- There is no overlapping of audit results.
- Larger audits can provide visibility to the hand-offs between departments.

Cons:
- Reinforces the idea of the audit as a major event instead of a normal process.
- Processes go for long stretches of time between audits.
- Auditors have fewer opportunities to practice their skills.
- Auditees never get comfortable being audited.
- Reinforces the idea of getting ready for the audit, instead of living the discipline.

Smaller, frequent audits throughout the year

Pros:
- Processes have frequent scrutiny.
- Improvements are generated on a continual basis.
- QMS discipline is maintained.

- Audits are less overwhelming.
- Auditors have plenty of practice opportunities.
- Auditors maintain higher energy levels.

Cons:
- Scheduling is more complex.
- Requires more frequent communications.
- Corrective actions overlap from one audit to the next, making tracking more challenging.

The first step to developing an audit schedule is to divide the organization into logical subgroups. The subgroups could be departments or processes. It's important to identify all the subgroups within the scope of the management system. Here is an example using a fictional organization.

Chemical Testing Labs Inc.

Chemical Testing Labs Inc. (CTLI) is a small company of 75 people that performs laboratory testing. Customers contact CTLI's customer service department to request quotes and lead times. After order booking, customers mail in samples to be tested and these are logged into CTLI's testing database. The testing is scheduled according to lead time, and testing is performed in the laboratory. The resulting data is subjected to a quality control function. Data is compiled into formal reports that are transmitted to the customers, typically via email.

Here are CTLI's processes/departments:
- Top management
- Business planning and risk management
- Customer service/sales
- Sample receiving
- Chemical lab
- Calibration
- Data quality control and reporting
- Competence, awareness, and communication
- Document and record control

- Purchasing
- Corrective action and improvement
- Internal auditing

As luck would have it, there are 12 processes identified. This makes it very easy to schedule one subgroup per month for auditing. The quality manager responsible for developing the schedule contacted the departments and gathered some important scheduling considerations:

- March and April are busy months for testing, so the chemical lab manager asked if these months could be avoided for auditing.
- Calibration could be audited as part of the chemical lab, but there are so many devices to be calibrated that it made sense to have a separate audit focused on this topic.
- The company president travels to Germany every year in August, so that month would need to be avoided for the top management audit.
- Each process was estimated to require from two to four hours to be audited. Once auditors were assigned to each audit, it would be their responsibility to contact the process owner and perform the audit.

The organization incorporated all these considerations into the audit schedule. The company also used a risk-based approach. In other words, not all the departments/processes were of equal importance. Some processes are audited twice a year. In our example, the quality manager determined that top management, corrective action, and the chemical lab were important processes. The audit schedule example in figure 5.1 shows how these were allocated over the calendar year. As you can see, May, July, and November each had two audits.

The schedule indicates that CTLI is a well-audited organization. Some department or process is audited every month. Thus, the QMS discipline is maintained and personnel are accustomed to being audited. Nobody takes the audit personally, and managers can respond effectively to corrective actions that result.

Figure 5.1 Sample internal audit schedule

Chemical Testing Labs Inc.—Internal Audit Schedule

Doc. Number:

Approved by:

Date: 3-24-XXXX

Area to be audited	Topics to be addressed	January	February	March	April	May	June	July	August	September	October	November	December
		1st Quarter			2nd Quarter			3rd Quarter			4th Quarter		
Top management*	Commitment, customer focus, policy, objectives, mgt review, improvement, roles responsibilities and authorities	xxx						xxx					
Business planning and risk management	Context, interested parties, scope, QMS processes, risks and opportunities		xxx										
Customer service/ Sales	Order booking, order review, complaint system, customer feedback			xxx									
Sample receiving	Incoming inspection, traceability, product identification				xxx								
Chemical lab*	Test methods, sample handling and storage, control of nonconforming products, lab quality statistics, traceability, lab safety					xxx						xxx	
Calibration	Periodic verification, internal calibration, external calibration, control of standards						xxx						

Figure 5.1   Sample internal audit schedule—continued

Chemical Testing Labs Inc.—Internal Audit Schedule

Doc. Number:

Approved by:

Date: 3-24-XXXX

Area to be audited	Topics to be addressed	January	February	March	April	May	June	July	August	September	October	November	December
		1st Quarter			2nd Quarter			3rd Quarter			4th Quarter		
Data QC and reporting	Data quality control, data interpretation, report formatting							xxx					
Competence, awareness, and communication	Competence requirements, training methods, records, verification of effectiveness								xxx				
Document and record control	Approval and issuance of documents, revisions, periodic review, location of records, retention times, preservation									xxx			
Purchasing	Purchase orders, evaluation of suppliers, supplier corrective actions, new supplier process										xxx		
Corrective action and improvement*	Sources of corrective action, tracking, identification of causes, actions taken, verification of effectiveness					xxx						xxx	
Internal auditing	Scheduling, training of auditors, planning, reporting, link to corrective action												xxx

* = Processes determined to have more importance

Figure 5.2					Sample internal audit schedule											

Chemical Testing Labs Inc.—Internal Audit Schedule

Doc. No.																
Approved by:																
Date: 3-24-XXXX			1st Quarter			2nd Quarter			3rd Quarter			4th Quarter			
Area to be audited	Duration	January	February	March	April	May	June	July	August	September	October	November	December
Spartanburg Plant and HQ	2 days	xxx					xxx						
Greenville Plant No. 1	2 days			xxx									
Greenville Plant No. 2	2 days					xxx							
Research and development center	1 day							xxx					
Highway 85 warehouse	2 days									xxx			
Customer service and sales offices	1 day											xxx	

* = Processes determined to have more importance

Allied Manufacturing LLC

Allied Manufacturing LLC is a large manufacturing company with multiple facilities. All the facilities are within a short drive of each other. The company has decided to maintain a corporate internal audit team instead of local audit teams at each facility. In this scenario, the audit schedule was divided up per plant locations instead of processes or departments. Even though the

scope is very different, the process of developing the schedule remains the same. First, we identify the areas to be audited:
- Spartanburg plant and headquarters
- Greenville plant No. 1
- Greenville plant No. 2
- Research and development center
- Highway 85 warehouse
- Customer service and sales offices

The six company locations coincide nicely with a bimonthly approach. The quality manager decided that the research and development center and the customer service and sales offices would require one day each. The remaining locations would require two days each. The quality manager factored the following considerations into the development of the audit schedule:
- December was avoided because so many people take vacation days at that time of year.
- Because many customer service agents were sent out for training in September, the director of sales asked for them not to be scheduled during that time.
- The Highway 85 warehouse is very busy in October and November getting shipments out, so they weren't scheduled for this time.

The plant deemed to be the most important was the Spartanburg plant and headquarters. For this reason, it was scheduled to receive two audits during the year. Most facilities go nearly a year between audits, however. This long duration could increase risk and weaken the QMS. Top management considered this and decided that the use of a key performance indicator (KPI) dashboard for each facility provided continual visibility into the facility's performance. Yearly internal audits—combined with the KPI dashboard—was deemed effective for maintaining the discipline of the QMS and giving a clear picture of operations.

Note that audit schedules are often periodically revised. The following events might cause the schedule to be revised:

- The addition of new processes or products
- Company acquisitions or divestitures
- Trends of audit findings
- Customer complaints
- Product failures and defects
- Failure to achieve objectives
- Relocation of operations

As you can see, these events are indicators that an organization's risk profile has changed. When this happens, it's necessary to refocus internal audits on the processes that have become less robust and weakened. Never fall into the trap of thinking that the audit schedule is a static document that only requires yearly scrutiny. Like any planning tool, it should be regularly revisited to ensure it provides the most effective allocation of resources.

FREQUENTLY ASKED QUESTIONS

Our audit schedule is only available upon request. Is that OK?

No. The audit schedule should be widely shared and discussed. There's nothing confidential about when audits will happen and what they will address.

Do we need to audit every ISO 9001 requirement in every single department?

No. Only audit the ISO 9001 requirements that apply in each department. For instance, it's unlikely that design requirements would apply to the warehouse.

Once our audit schedule is published, it's never revised during the year. Is this OK?

Unlikely. Changes will happen during the year that will most likely require changes in the audit schedule. Also, certain processes will underperform during audits, which will require additional scrutiny.

Chapter 6

Auditable Requirements

Auditable requirements and objective evidence are at the heart of every audit. In fact, auditors can't function without a full understanding of these concepts. They work together to produce a complete picture of how the organization performs.

Let's begin with auditable requirements. These are the obligations that the organization has committed to implementing. Most of an audit is spent verifying that requirements have been met. Here is an example of a requirement: "Technicians must have the customer sign the work order after repairs have been completed."

Let's say for the sake of illustration that this requirement originated from a company procedure. The company wrote the procedure because managers deemed this requirement (and others) to be important. We can't see the entire procedure, but there are doubtless requirements before this one and probably some after it. During the preparation phase of an audit, the auditor requests various procedures and documents from the organization. The auditor analyzes these to determine which requirements are worth verifying during the audit. An auditor doesn't verify every requirement in every procedure; this would result in an audit that lasts months. Rather, an auditor chooses what he or she believes to be the most important requirements to verify. Inexperienced auditors always struggle with what requirements they should focus on. Here are some thoughts to guide you:

- Requirements for key production processes
- Requirements for inspecting product/service

- Requirements related to potentially dangerous tasks
- Requirements for reviewing information and making improvements
- Requirements related to known weaknesses and problem areas
- Requirements that come directly from customers

There are thousands of requirements the organization must satisfy, and they come from a dizzying range of sources. However, auditors should only focus on the requirements that are within the audit's scope. The scope is the boundary of the audit. For instance, if I'm doing an ISO 9001 audit, I'm probably not going to pay much attention to regulatory requirements about used oil disposal. Because the requirement is related to environmental regulatory compliance, it's not within the scope of most ISO 9001 audits.

The other caveat related to requirements is that company management must officially approve them. If we're talking about a company procedure or document, the approval usually comes from some sort of signature or other sign-off. If we're talking about a standard such as ISO 9001, the approval comes from top management making an official declaration to pursue certification to the standard. Usually, only officially approved requirements are available to you before and during the audit. If you stick to these, you will be fine.

Let's talk about several different requirements that are likely to be used during an audit.

COMPANY PROCEDURES AND REQUIREMENTS

This group constitutes the largest category of requirements during most internal audits. They are documents written by the company itself to address its specific needs. They can be long or short, graphic or text, simple or complex. There is no right or wrong way to write a procedure, and they should not be written for the convenience of auditors. The auditor should request company procedures prior to the audit and attempt to understand them during his or her preparation time. This preparation time could be 30 minutes or eight hours. It all depends on how many requirements are within the audit's scope and the auditor's familiarity with the organization.

Organizations use a wide range of names to refer to their documents. Some have formal categories of documents that relate to different degrees of detail. For instance, you may encounter a company that has a category called "operating procedures" and a category called "work instructions." Historically, an operating procedure addresses a process from a high level, covering broad systematic requirements. For instance, you may find a document called "Calibration Operating Procedure." This is likely to be a high-level document that covers the entire calibration process and how it's managed.

On the other hand, a work instruction is usually a much lower level document. It addresses tasks from a hands-on level. For example, you might encounter a caliper calibration work instruction. This might provide a step-by-step process on how to calibrate a caliper. Please note that organizations aren't required to have different levels of documents. I only mention it so that you can be aware of different approaches that companies may take.

Besides procedures and work instructions, there are many different "procedural" documents that an organization may decide write. These include:

- Flowcharts
- Checklists
- Process descriptions
- Set-up sheets
- Process standards
- Test methods
- Standard operating procedures (SOPs)

The list goes on and on. As an auditor, you will never be 100 percent familiar with all documents written by the organization. How could you? Your challenge is to do a reasonable amount of preparation so that you can ask meaningful questions during the audit. Some company documents will only rear their heads during the audit, especially in the case with very low-level instructions. You will use these as you see fit based on their apparent importance and risk.

Finally, organizations differ widely in how many procedural documents they write. Some have dozens or even hundreds of documents addressing their specific requirements. Others maintain far fewer, even to the point of having no procedures at all, and simply rely on employee competency to produce effective results. You may have opinions about how many procedures an organization should have, but it's up to the organization to decide how much documentation it needs to manage operations.

COMPANY POLICIES AND OBJECTIVES

Policies are an organization's highest-level documents. They rarely include procedural content (i.e., "how to"), but most often address overall company direction, philosophy, and goals. Because policies are so high level, they can be very difficult to audit against. Nonetheless, the audit must include policies. The ISO 9001 framework requires a quality policy.

Auditors should examine the commitments stated in policies and ask how the high-level commitments are deployed to all levels of the organization. A hollow commitment that nobody understands is worthless. If you read a policy that includes a statement such as, "We are committed to becoming the leader in technological innovation," top managers should be asked how they're working toward that commitment. Look for specific evidence that lower-level employees also understand the commitments and can explain how they support the policies.

Objectives are also high-level documents, though they have a sharper edge than most policies. Objectives state metrics and measurable goals that the company is pursuing. Here are some examples:

- Reduce warranty repairs to less than 1 percent of sales.
- Achieve 97 percent on-time shipping.
- Perform all service calls within two hours of scheduled appointment.
- Reduce scrap by 5 percent.
- Increase sales by 10 percent.

As an auditor, you're concerned about what sort of plans are behind the objectives. Has the organization determined necessary resources, planned actions, identified responsibilities, and established timelines? Ultimately, is the organization making progress against each objective? If not, what is the organization doing about it? Inherent in the presence of objectives is the obligation to work toward them systematically.

STANDARD REQUIREMENTS

Most management systems that use internal auditing are based on a standard of some sort. The most common standard is ISO 9001, but there are many others. These standards are designed to apply to a wide variety of organizations, which tends to make them a little difficult to interpret. For this reason, standard requirements are sometimes deemphasized during internal audits. This is a mistake. If an organization has implemented a management system standard, then internal audits must include its requirements.

Requirements in standards such as ISO 9001 are written as "shall" statements. They are sometimes very specific and sometimes quite vague. Understanding the practical interpretations of a standard represents a specific training need for most internal auditors. When auditors apply standard requirements, they often find that they must explain the requirement to the auditee.

Sometimes auditors find that there are two nearly identical requirements: one from the applicable standard and one from a company document. When this happens, the requirement to use is the lowest-level requirement. In other words, the requirement written by the organization. Why would an auditor want to use the company requirement instead of a standard requirement? Because it has more specific relevance to the organization. It felt strongly enough about that topic to address it in its procedures, so any issues raised by the auditor on that topic presumably will grab the organization's attention.

RECORDS

Auditors sometimes overlook records as sources of requirements during an audit. After all, records are historical; they describe what happened in the past. Sometimes this includes past decisions that must be acted upon. Good auditors will identify these commitments and verify that they've taken place. Examples of records often used during audits include:

- *Purchase orders.* Purchase orders include requirements that suppliers must meet. This also obligates the organization to verify that the supplier did met its requirements. An example is the requirement, "Shipment must include certified test results." The auditor should verify that the shipment included certified test results and that the test results met all requirements.

- *Management review records.* Top management should lead these meetings, which nearly always include action items to implement. Auditors should scan these records for action items and seek evidence of completion.
- *Corrective action records.* Corrective actions are the formal problem-solving events for organizations. They will always include improvement actions. Auditors must verify that improvements have been fully implemented and checked for effectiveness.
- *Sales orders and contracts.* Sales records always include product/service requirements that the organization must fulfill. These could include delivery dates, performance requirements, dimensional specifications, or any number of other variables. Auditors should confirm that employees know about these requirements and that the organization is meeting all of them.

VERBAL REQUIREMENTS

Verbal requirements show up occasionally during audits. They're not used very often, but are more common in organizations that use documentation very lightly. These are statements made by people who have responsibility and authority over the process in question. You would never choose to use a verbal requirement during an audit if there was already a documented requirement. Here are some examples of verbal requirements:

- The plant manager stated, "We shut down at 4:00 every Thursday afternoon and do a complete cleaning of the facility." The documentation doesn't mention cleaning, but the plant manager stated that the cleaning was an established routine that everybody knew about.
- The lab manager stated, "Latex samples must be delivered to the lab by the chemist. No other employees are allowed inside the lab." All personnel have been told of this requirement, but it's not documented anywhere.
- The director of technical services stated, "Technicians must perform follow-up calls within 48 hours of all repairs." Technicians discuss the follow-up calls in the weekly technical meeting, and the process for performing follow-up is outlined in orientation training.

In all three cases, there was an established process, but no documentation to support it. The person making the statement had the responsibility and authority over the process in question, and the statement was expected to be followed. If these conditions are met, then an auditor could use the statement as a requirement during an audit.

AUDITING AGAINST OPINIONS

Everybody has opinions. Sometimes the opinions even make sense. But opinions don't constitute requirements. The one thing that's never used as a requirement is an auditor's opinion. The irony of opinions is that the more auditing you do, the more likely you are to develop strong opinions. Auditors must always guard against using their opinions during audits. Opinions are part of a whole family of entities that have no place in most audits, including:

- Opinions
- Best practices
- Neat ideas
- World-class methods
- "What we used to do at my old company"

If you see something during the audit that seems like the wrong way to do things, your job is to find a requirement that covers the area in question. Your opinion of what's right or wrong isn't enough.

Most audit systems have a category of finding that falls short of a nonconformity. These go by various names, including "observation," "concern," "recommendation," and "opportunity for improvement." These types of findings generally don't require the organization to take corrective action. As such, the findings don't require a solid requirement and can be based on the opinion of an auditor. But nonconformities are never based on auditor opinions.

TRACEABLE REQUIREMENTS

All requirements used during the audit must be traceable. In other words, you say where each requirement comes from. Requirements without traceability have no credibility or context. When identifying a requirement, define the following elements:

- Document name (where the requirement comes from)
- Document number
- Revision level
- Section number/title
- The exact requirement, taken word-for-word from the source

Here is an example of a well-written requirement, along with the evidence that makes it a nonconformity:

- *Requirement:* The Finishing Procedure (SOP #QOP-32, revision 3) states in section 6.5 that employees must wear white gloves when handling finished product.
- *Evidence:* The auditor observed two employees in the warehouse handling a pallet of finished product (part #443) without white gloves.

This provides the perfect transition to our next chapter: Objective Evidence.

FREQUENTLY ASKED QUESTIONS

Can a nonconformity be written against an "implied" requirement?

No. A requirement is either real or it's not. The notion of an "implied" requirement just introduces subjectivity into the process. Stick to using explicit requirements that the organization has formally committed to.

We were told by our registrar that our auditors should mainly focus on our company procedures during audits. Is this correct?

Not exactly. Company procedures probably comprise the largest category of requirements, but there are many other sources of requirements. Auditors should sample requirements from a variety of sources.

I found a document on the internet that I believe should apply to the organization. Can I use this during the audit?

No, not unless the company has formally included this document within its management system.

Chapter 7

Objective Evidence

O bjective evidence is proof that the organization did—or didn't— meet its requirements. One of the primary objectives of an audit is to collect objective evidence. Not just random objective evidence, but evidence specific to the requirements in the audit. The auditor selects requirements to verify and then looks for objective evidence that the organization met them.

Objective evidence has a couple of specific purposes. First, it provides credibility to the audit process. By keeping evidence of facts gathered during the audit, we can be confident that an audit occurred. The auditor didn't just go through the motions. Real people were interviewed, records were examined, and current processes were analyzed. Anybody can review the evidence and feel confident that the audit was effective. Second, the evidence forms the raw material for any nonconformities. We're not seeking nonconformities; we're seeking conformity. Despite this goal, nonconformities are a common outcome of audits. If we collect detailed evidence during the audit, we'll be able to write clear and defensible nonconformities.

Objective evidence also helps to write meaningful positive findings. Both outputs—nonconformities and positive findings—rely on accurate and objective evidence gathered by you, the auditor.

CHARACTERISTICS OF OBJECTIVE EVIDENCE

The term "objective evidence" sounds rather complicated, but it's very simple. Here are the characteristics of objective evidence:

- *Unbiased.* Objective evidence is unbiased. It's not clouded by your emotions or feelings. You gather the evidence in a completely neutral way. Bias often arises when you have a personal relationship with an interviewee. Auditors must be aware of how their personal relationships influence the way they view evidence. If an auditor believes he or she is becoming biased, the auditor has the responsibility to approach the lead auditor or quality manager and make this known.

- *Factual.* Objective evidence is factual. That means it's real, not made up or imagined. Very few auditors intentionally create nonfactual evidence. Occasionally, auditors misinterpret evidence. This is one of the many benefits of auditing in pairs of auditors. When you are with somebody else, you can always ask his or her opinion of the evidence you're examining. This should keep you solidly in the realm of factual evidence.

- *First hand.* Objective evidence is personally observed. The evidence is seen, heard, read, or experienced by the auditor. A good auditor never relies on second- or third-hand information, as it's often distorted. The more hand-offs in an information chain, the less the information can be trusted.

- *Traceable.* Objective evidence is traceable. That means you include all the identifiers about the evidence. Identifiers could include the date, time, part number, department name, or anything else that lets the organization know where the evidence came from. In theory, audit evidence should be traceable enough that anybody could go see the same thing that you saw during the audit.

- *Impersonal.* Objective evidence is impersonal. The evidence is presented to reinforce a focus on systems and processes, instead of people. Names are omitted from evidence, and job titles are used instead. No opinions about the severity or possible effects of evidence are included. The evidence is written neutrally.

Just because your evidence is subjective doesn't mean that's the end of the line. You can often turn subjective evidence into objective evidence by doing some additional digging. This is called following an audit trail. You might start out with biased or second-hand information, and then convert it to objective evidence by asking a few more questions.

EVIDENCE GATHERING

Evidence gathering is the heart of auditing. One of the themes of this book is that effective auditors are naturally curious and enter every audit with the goal of learning something from it. I can't stress this enough. When you want to learn, your mind will crave information and your senses will be especially sharp. Very little will escape your detection. Armed with the desire to expand my own knowledge, I ask probing questions and pursue unique and important lines of inquiry. You can't fake the desire to learn. It exists solely inside your head. There are certain truths that you can remind yourself of that will help put you in this state of mind.

- *This company is doing a lot of things RIGHT.* In today's extremely competitive economy, bad companies don't survive. You can assume that any company in operation must be doing at least a few things correctly.
- *The people here are interesting and have some fascinating stories to tell me.* I have found this to be true 100 percent of the time. No matter how banal and commonplace an organization seems, it will include some people who absolutely fascinate me. They have interesting things to tell me, and I have a hard time pulling myself away from them.
- *I will learn a lot during this audit.* There are processes, technologies, and products here that I've never seen before. Yes, I'm here to do an audit, but the benefits of the audit will flow in both directions. If I'm perceptive, I will learn as much from them as they will learn from me.
- *I am a partner of the organization, not an adversary.* You aren't looking for nonconformities. You are looking for ways that the organization can improve. This is a subtle but important difference. At no time should an auditor portray the audit as a sport in which the objective is to rack up nonconformities. The number of nonconformities is inconsequential.

What matters is that the company knows what it needs to focus on. The auditor is the "optometrist" that enables this clear vision.

- *The evidence I gather should focus on the big picture.* Auditing is a process of details. My task is to accumulate the details into trends that will help the organization improve. I need to probe beneath the surface and uncover the true strengths and weaknesses of the organization. I will only be able to do this once the organization trusts me and understands that I am there to help.

The overall impression you should give the organization is trust. Every word and mannerism you evoke as an auditor should reinforce the idea that you can be trusted. People who are trying to learn can usually be trusted because learning is a cooperative process that requires a two-way exchange of information. Be a learner and you will also be an effective auditor.

Once your mind is ready to learn, you're ready to begin gathering evidence. How do you do this? It's such an intuitive and simple process that a child could gather evidence as part of an audit. It is a mix of techniques that are used interchangeably: visual observation, examination of records, and employee interviews. One moment you will be looking around the work area, and the very next moment you'll ask an employee a question. The audit is a skillfully woven fabric of these techniques. Let's take a deeper look at each major technique used for gathering evidence.

VISUAL OBSERVATION

This is the most basic way to gather evidence during an audit. Simply looking around is a powerful way to understand how an organization works. Is the place organized or cluttered? Is communication formal or informal? A smart auditor immerses himself or herself in the organization and looks at it from every angle. Here are some especially powerful examples of evidence to look for:

- *Uncontrolled documents.* Look around for "bandit documents" posted on walls, machines, and desks. These are often uncontrolled, informal specs or procedures. Bandit documents often take the form of sticky notes, marker settings written on machines, old memos, printed e-mails, and photocopies of external documents. If the document provides information on product requirements, process control guidelines, or decision-making criteria, you need to inquire how the information is supposed to be controlled.

- *Product outside the normal flow.* Look for stacks of product that appear to be outside the normal flow of production. These are often nonconforming products, separated so they can be addressed later. If you find nonconforming products, ensure they're handled in accordance with the company's process for controlling nonconforming products.

- *Measuring instruments.* The presence of measuring instruments usually means that there are important characteristics that must be verified. When you see measuring instruments, you need to find out what they're used for. If we're using them to check product, verify service, or control a process, the organization should have a process for ensuring the fitness of the instruments. These range from complex measurement devices to include very simple gauges (templates, patterns, jigs, rulers, tape measures, and limit samples), and everything in between.

- *Housekeeping and organization.* It doesn't take an expert to identify a mess. That's really what you're looking for. Problems with housekeeping and clutter are symptoms of larger issues. Delve deeper into these conditions and try to discover what's happening. Lack of housekeeping often points to issues with product preservation, defects, identification, and traceability.

- *Product identification.* Verify that all products have some sort of identification. Identification could be achieved through a variety of methods such as stickers; tags; bar codes; serial numbers; assigned location; special bins, boxes, or bags; or many other means. If you're not clear what the identification is, ask someone in the area.

- *Improvised fixes and repairs.* Look for evidence that employees have had to make improvised fixes and repairs. Amateur repairs often use duct tape, rope, shims, and other crude methods. Improvised repairs could be evidence that the maintenance program isn't properly performed or that management isn't providing adequate resources.

- *Informal recordkeeping.* Look for informal recordkeeping in notebooks, logbooks, or scratch sheets of paper, etc. If the records relate to anything that ISO 9001 or the company's management system addresses, they should be handled in a formal manner.

EXAMINATION OF RECORDS

Records are historical artifacts and auditors generally accept them as statements of fact. If we have a credible record that indicates something happened, we can usually conclude the action happened. Of course, records aren't required of everything that happens in an organization. If a company procedure or a standard (such as ISO 9001) requires a record, then, obviously, we need a record.

I mentioned the need for "credible" records. What exactly is a credible record? It's one that we can have faith in as being an accurate representation of the activities it vouches for. These are some characteristics that help make a record credible:

- *Complete.* If the record starts as a blank form, then we would expect all spaces to be completed. Any blanks should have clear explanations for the omission.
- *Dates.* Records need verifiable dates to have any credibility.
- *Participants.* If the record was a meeting, then a listing of participants would help tell the story of what happened. If the record was simply proof of something happening, it must include the name of the person who performed it.
- *Actual results.* What actions took place? If the record was proof of inspection, then the inspection results would be required. If the record was taken from a meeting, what was decided?
- *Subsequent actions.* Many records will include action items or follow-ups. If the activity being recorded includes these types of actions, the record should clearly indicate it.

EMPLOYEE INTERVIEWS

An interview is a structured discussion. Unlike a normal discussion that can meander over a wide variety of topics, an interview has a specific objective. Your objective, of course, is capturing factual information about the process being audited. The interviewer must plan and control the discussion so the required facts are gathered in the most efficient manner possible. In general, certain cues help an auditor know if an interview can be considered objective evidence:

- The employee makes statements relating to things he or she personally saw or took part in.
- The employee's statements relate directly to his or her responsibilities and authorities.
- The employee's statements can be corroborated by records or supporting statements from other personnel.
- The employee makes specific statements that include credible details.

In cases where there are requirements for records, then a statement alone would not suffice.

EVIDENCE SAMPLING

Audits are never 100 percent inspections. How could they be? There isn't enough time to examine everything in an organization. Instead, audits sample evidence. The sample doesn't need to be statistically based, but it does need to be representative. If a population of evidence includes thousands of records, then a representative sample would certainly be more than one. Just take a reasonable sample of evidence given the evidence available. Think about how you might divide the overall population of evidence into rational subgroups. For instance, if you're auditing training, you might divide employees into top management, hourly, employees who have worked there for less than 90 days, and employees with more than 10 years of experience. Then you'll take your samples from the subgroups, instead of just blindly selecting samples from the overall population.

RECORDING NOTES

Note taking is a very important part of the audit process. Evidence gathered must be fully traceable and highly detailed. This means that auditors must develop efficient means for capturing their notes. If you're the sort of person who takes notes during an interview, make sure to tell your auditee that you'll be writing down details. Also, remember that you likely have one chance to capture the details of evidence. Slow down, take your time, and write the required details and evidence traceability while you're in the department. The one thing you would never do is ask an auditee to speak into an audio recorder. This makes the audit seem too much like a police interrogation.

EXAMPLES OF EVIDENCE

The best way to understand good vs. bad evidence is to study examples. Here's what appears to be a detailed statement of facts. Read it carefully and decide what you don't like about it:

"Returned goods were missing the nonconforming materials tags, which greatly increases the chance of accidentally shipping bad material."

This evidence has several problems, including the facts that it's highly subjective and not traceable. Here are the specifics:

- Where was this found? The area or department should be indicated.
- What returned goods are we talking about? We need to identify them to enable traceability. Part numbers or descriptions should be adequate.
- How many returned goods were missing the tags? The quantity helps put the situation in perspective.
- The auditor has included an opinion at the end. This adds subjectivity to the evidence and will only inflame the auditee.

Let's rework the evidence. Here are the same facts, expressed in much more complete terms:

"Three out of 10 returned desk kits (product code 675) in the warehouse hold area were missing the nonconforming materials tags."

Here is why it's better:

- The area where the returned goods were located is clearly indicated (i.e., warehouse hold area).
- The identity of the returned goods is provided (i.e., desk kits, product code 675).

- The sample size is shown, helping the audited organization understand the magnitude of the situation (i.e., three out of 10).
- Only facts are stated. No auditor opinions about effects or ramifications of the nonconformity are included.

SEEKING EVIDENCE OF POSITIVES

Smart auditors always ask themselves, "Am I actively looking for positives during the audit?" The audit should be a balanced snapshot of the organization. Balanced includes the identification of positive practices, as well as nonconformities. Any organization still in business in these tough economic times is doing a lot of things right. Too often, audits become an obsessive exercise in finding the organization's flaws. As you can imagine, audits of this sort are rarely welcomed or requested.

You should continually remind yourself to be on the lookout for positives during an audit. Ask yourself these questions during the audit:

- What sets this organization apart?
- What does it do especially well?
- What practices create competitive advantage?
- Where are the pockets of excellence?
- Who are the innovators of new methods and tools?

If you are leading an audit, remind the other auditors under your supervision to be on the lookout for positives and best practices.

It's important to note that in mature management systems, identification of positives is one of the most important aspects of an audit. That's because the discipline of the management system is well established. Audits have already picked the low-hanging fruit, so auditors can turn their attention to finding the isolated pockets of excellence. These are often difficult to see, so an important purpose of the audit is to root them out. Once identified, these best practices can be widely adapted. This motivates people to embrace the audit process while driving improvement throughout the organization.

Here are some example positive findings:

- Clean and well-organized receiving area
- Management of the lab is fully engaged

- Effective corrective actions generated by production
- Detailed action plans for achieving objectives in the purchasing department

Try to write individualized positives that are specific to the areas they relate to. We have no use for the generic and generalized. Remember, we're looking for best practices that the rest of the organization can learn from. Keep your eyes open for positives, and you'll find that you produce better results and are always welcome on site.

FREQUENTLY ASKED QUESTIONS

A very credible employee provided evidence about another employee. The employee isn't an auditor. Can we write the nonconformity based on what he told us?

No. This is second-hand evidence, also known as hearsay. Auditors collect their own evidence directly from first-hand sources.

I wrote a nonconformity, but the auditee provided evidence later during the audit that the company actually met the requirement. Should I withdraw the nonconformity?

Yes. If the company has evidence that it met the requirement in question, then the nonconformity should be withdrawn.

Our auditors found evidence that a particular problem was widespread. Can we just say that the evidence was found everywhere, instead of listing the specific locations?

No. Objective evidence is always traceable. Create a bulleted list of the specific locations. This will build credibility of the audit process and help managers understand the scope of the nonconformity.

Chapter 8

Interviewing Techniques

Audit interviewing should be nothing more than a friendly conversation. It's not an interrogation, a deposition, or trial. It's a simple, friendly chat about how we're doing as an organization. Everything you do during an audit interview should reinforce this perception. This approach establishes a connection with the people you are interviewing and allows you to get all the information you need.

Most of the evidence you gather during an audit comes from employees. You might examine processes, products, tools, equipment, documents, or records, but ultimately *people* make these available to you. These people provide details and clarifications about what you're examining, and they answer follow-up questions. The way you speak to them and respond to their information will greatly influence their level of enthusiasm and cooperation.

Like any communication, interviewing is highly individualized. Each person has his or her own unique communication style, along with personalized techniques. Differing styles aside, here are some basic principles that will guide you toward effective interviewing in any audit:

- *Put yourself in a learning state of mind prior to auditing.* Your state of mind during the audit strongly influences your interviewing skills. If you begin the audit with the idea that you're going to learn some interesting things from some fascinating people, you will naturally be more engaged. You will interact on a more conversational level, just like you would with friends. This is exactly the way you want to behave during the audit. Of course, the audit isn't just a free-flowing conversation. It has very specific lines of questions and informational goals, but you still want to conduct the audit conversationally.

- *Introduce yourself and explain your purpose.* During an audit, I'm always amazed by the employees who have no idea who I am or what I'm doing. Of course, I ask managers and supervisors to let their employees know in advance that I am coming, but somehow the message gets lost in the shuffle. That's why it's critical that the first words out of your mouth need to be a friendly greeting, followed by an introduction of who you are and that you're doing an audit. If you're interviewing hourly employees, you may not even want to use the term "audit." It can have a very negative connotation. Replace the words "performing an audit" with "talking to employees about our processes." This sounds like a more cooperative event and it makes it clear that nobody is being personally evaluated.

- *Ask if they have a few minutes to talk.* This is simply a courtesy. Responding to interview questions—no matter how skillfully delivered—will only distract employees while they're working. Make sure your interview won't prevent important work from getting done. If you are being escorted by a departmental representative, your escort will help you select an employee who has enough time to talk. Asking the question "Do you have a few minutes to talk?" also gives the employee a degree of control. The great majority of the time the employee will respond favorably, but knowing that it's his or her choice removes some of the fear from the process. Everybody likes to have some control over what is happening to them, even in the context of a friendly conversation.

- *Put the auditee at ease.* A nervous or frightened employee isn't going to contribute much to a conversation. When you begin talking to someone during an audit, you must immediately begin evaluating his or her demeanor. If the employee is smiling, at ease, and clearly comfortable, you have nothing to worry about. The employee has probably been interviewed before or isn't easily intimidated. On the other hand, if the employee is avoiding eye contact, fidgeting, shaking, or unable to speak clearly, he or she might be frightened by speaking to an auditor. Investing a minute or two in building a relationship can help remove the fear. You can ask how long the person has worked there and if he or she has worked in different areas of the company. Ask about family photos if they're present. I'm not above asking about somebody's pretty earrings or cool shirt. Do whatever it takes to create a relationship, but remember that you only have a couple of minutes to spare. Even more important, keep in mind that you must take a genuine interest in the person you're speaking with. This is not the time to "fake it." I'm lucky that I find just about everybody interesting in some way, so it's easy for me to find something to talk about that helps us build a connection. Break the ice and you'll be amazed at how readily you get the information you need during your interview. Finally, I find it very helpful to remind the auditee that the audit is about the process and our procedures, not about him or her.

- *Start with basic questions.* I like to begin the informational part of the interview with very basic questions. These are usually open-ended questions for which there is no right or wrong answer. They include such inquiries as:
  ✓ Please tell me about the work you do.
  ✓ What types of products do you produce?
  ✓ Can you give me a brief overview of the process?

  Questions of this sort put the ball entirely in the employee's court. The employee can respond with a little or a lot of information, and this sets the stage for follow-up questions. Sometimes the "brief overview of the process" triggers so many follow-up questions that I never get to use the checklist that I prepared in advance. The audit trails present themselves to me like gold-paved walkways. The basic questions also tend to lubricate the employee's brain and prepare them for the more detailed questions that will inevitably result.

- *Test the process with "what if" questions.* The beginning of the interview educates you about the process. Some of the information you may already know from your audit preparation and general understanding of the process, but some will likely be entirely new knowledge. This enhanced comprehension gives you an excellent base from which to ask theoretical questions. These test the true effectiveness of the process. Most processes are designed to do one thing reasonably well. A truly robust process can handle a variety of different activities and respond to unforeseen problems. Figure 8.1 illustrates examples of what-if questions.

Figure 8.1	Theoretical questions
Process step	**"What if" question**
Raw material always arrives with a certificate of analysis.	What if the raw materials arrive without the certificate?
The measuring instrument has a calibration sticker showing it has been checked.	What if the measuring instrument is missing the calibration sticker?
The work order must include the customer's purchase order.	What if the work order is missing the purchase order number?
The technician's signature indicates the data has been checked.	What if the report arrives at your desk without the technician's signature?

Sometimes the what-if question leads to important information; sometimes it doesn't. Your friendly discussion about the process is designed to find potential process improvements. Keep the discussion focused on the process and make it very clear that you're not evaluating employee performance.

- *Use your checklist and follow the audit trails.* Your audit checklist is an insurance policy of sorts. It provides you with a reminder of relevant questions that can be used as needed. If I'm very lucky during an audit, then the friendly conversation I'm having with the employee provides me with all sorts of follow-up questions and audit trails. An audit trail is simply a nugget of information that makes you think that there could be a problem with a process. You follow the audit trail by asking related questions and digging deeper. Most checklists provide an entry question. Then it's up to the auditor to recognize a potential weakness. The follow-up questions probably won't be on your audit checklist, but they follow logically from the flow of conversation. Figure 8.2 shows examples of questions and answers that begin with simple checklist questions and proceed to an audit trail.

Figure 8.2	Indications for potential audit trails
Auditor	[Looking at his audit checklist] "The procedure says that all jobs must include a parts list. Do you have an example of a parts list?"
Employee	"Sure, here's the parts list from the job I'm working on now." [Shows the auditor the parts list]
Auditor	"Thanks." [Looking at his audit checklist again] "I understand that the parts list is supposed to be signed. Is this one signed?"
Employee	[Examining the parts list] "Yes, it's signed right there. On this job, the receiving clerk signed the parts list. Usually the expeditor signs it."
Auditor	"Does that make a difference?" [Beginning to follow the audit trail]
Employee	"Well, it could make a difference. The receiving clerk does not know the required parts as well as the expeditor. I guess it's possible that he could miss something."
Auditor	"Did the clerk miss anything on this parts list?"
Employee	"I don't think so. This is a product that we make a lot of. The only thing I'm not too certain about is the type of bearing that this product requires."
Auditor	[Looking at the parts list] "I see that it says bearing style No. 155. Is that correct?"
Employee	"I'm really not sure. The only way to know for sure is to bring up the engineering drawing. The expeditor has access to all the drawings."
Auditor	"Can you access the engineering drawing?"
Employee	[Nods at a computer terminal] "Sure, they're on the password-protected part of the server. I can sign-in using my password. [Types on the keyboard. A moment later, an engineering drawing appears on the screen.]
Auditor	"Thanks. Is that the engineering drawing for the product you're making?'
Employee	"Yes, that's it."
Auditor	"What bearing style does it say is required?"
Employee	"Hmm. Well, that's funny. It says that bearing style No. 201 is required."
Auditor	"Not what is shown on the parts list?"

Figure 8.2	Indications for potential audit trails— continued
Employee	"Correct. The parts list is wrong. It says bearing style No. 155, but the actual bearing that is required is style No. 201."
Auditor	"Based on what we've seen, I'm going to write this up as a nonconformity. Not against you, of course, but against the process."
Employee	"Sure. You definitely need to do that. We need to make sure we don't make any more mistakes like this again."

In figure 8.2 the auditor followed the audit trail all the way to its conclusion. In this case, the conclusion was a nonconformity. Both the auditor and the employee recognized the issue as a nonconformity, and the auditor made it clear that the issue was not an indictment of anybody's performance. It was simply an opportunity for improving the process. Granted, not every audit nonconformity works out so smoothly, and not every trail produces a clear opportunity. The trick is recognizing when a trail presents itself and being able to follow it.

- *Be an active listener.* Active listening is one of the most basic communication skills, and it certainly applies to audit interviewing. It's the state of being fully engaged in a conversation. Active listening can mean a wide range of things, but in general it is the conversion of passive listening into a more robust state of interactivity. You become an active participant instead of just being a receiver. Here are the most typical behaviors that demonstrate it:

  ✓ Maintaining eye contact
  ✓ Nodding and providing other nonverbal signals of listening
  ✓ Focusing on what is being said and not "zoning out"
  ✓ Repeating key details back to confirm understanding
  ✓ Attempting to interpret the speaker's nonverbal communication
  ✓ Asking appropriate follow-up questions
  ✓ Encouraging additional information
  ✓ Providing clues throughout that the communicator's message is being received

Active listening comes naturally to most people. Auditors just have to remind themselves that it's a key technique for maximizing the information they receive.

- *Confirm any nonconformities.* A nonconformity is a failure to meet a requirement. If you think you've uncovered a nonconformity during an interview, it's important to confirm all the details right then and there. The best way to do this is to break the nonconformity into small pieces. The two main pieces of a nonconformity are the requirement and the evidence. First, confirm that you and the employee agree on the meaning of the requirement. If the requirement is a procedure, discuss the relevant part of the procedure and make sure that you and the employee share the same interpretation. If the requirement is ISO 9001, discuss what the requirement means in practical terms and how it's applied within the organization. Second, confirm that you both interpret the evidence the same way. Discuss the specifics of what was seen, heard, read, or experienced. Doing this while the information is still fresh and the evidence still present is essential.

Smart auditors avoid grand pronouncements such as, "I believe we have a nonconformity!" This automatically sets up a confrontational situation and almost guarantees that the auditor will get some resistance, no matter how clear the facts are. Much wiser is a calm and measured statement such as, "I believe we have an opportunity here. Let's talk about it." This opens the door to a logical discussion of the requirement and the evidence. The focus remains on improving the process. Of course, at the end of the day the auditor and the organization will both agree that we indeed do have a nonconformity.

- *Compliment all positives* Good auditors find a lot of positives. Why? Because they're not looking for nonconformities. Good auditors are simply seeking evidence that the organization is meeting requirements. In the process of doing this, they often find nonconformities. They also find positives. If the organization has a mature management system with fully engaged employees, there could be a lot of positives. When you see a positive, compliment it right away. This acknowledges the effort, initiative, and intelligence of the organization's employees. It also creates a spirit of cooperation and trust. Employees realize that you're not just there to write nonconformities. When employees really trust the auditors, they will openly provide the needed evidence. Sometimes they even point out nonconformities that auditors missed. Why would they do such a thing? Because they know the auditors are on their side and that there's no risk in being completely candid. They know they have a partner is creating improvement.

- *Thank the auditee.* The final step of any interview is to thank the person you've been talking with. The thanks should be warm and genuine, and it's best when accompanied with a smile. The goal is to leave the employee with the impression that you are someone who was a pleasure to talk to, even as you probed the employee's work processes. If you leave employees with that impression, you'll be welcomed back with open arms.

ADDITIONAL INTERVIEW SITUATIONS

Employees sometimes want to argue about whether a situation is a nonconformity. Don't get bogged down in these debates. Your job as an auditor is to be fair and balanced and to bring all issues to the attention of the organization. If someone wants to debate a nonconformity with me, I break the nonconformity into two pieces and get agreement on both halves. It's much easier to argue about broad issues than specific issues. Figure 8.3 demonstrates how these discussions usually proceed.

Another situation that occasionally happens is that an employee offers unsolicited information. In other words, they tell you things you didn't ask about. The unsolicited information is usually hearsay about other departments or processes. "Hey, you ought to go check out the guys in the sales department. They never follow the standard price list." Obviously, this type of information is not objective evidence. You won't write a nonconformity on such subjective evidence, but you might decide to investigate further. The decision to investigate further is usually a factor of these variables:

- Does the issue represent significant risk? If the answer is yes, and the issue could harm the organization or its customers in some meaningful way, then it's probably worth exploring.

Figure 8.3	Resistance on a nonconformity
Employee	"I don't believe this should be a nonconformity. It's silly."
Auditor	"OK, let's talk about it. Do you agree that the procedure states that finished products must be handled with cotton gloves?" [I'm getting agreement on the first half of the nonconformity, which is the requirement.]
Employee	"Yeah, I guess so."
Auditor	"Very good. Do you also agree that we saw an employee in the finishing area handing finished product without cotton gloves?" [Now I'm getting agreement on the second half of the nonconformity, which is the evidence.]
Employee	"Yeah, we saw that."
Auditor	"Excellent. We're both in total agreement."
Employee	"I suppose so."

- Does the issue fall within the scope of the audit? If the answer is no, then the auditor will usually not stray into that territory. The audit scope sets the boundaries of the audit.
- Do we have time to pursue the issue? Audits are always a balance of resources, and your number one resource is time. If the audit is already full, with no gaps that could accommodate the following of audit trails, then it's a moot point.

Most interview situations require a mix of open-ended and closed-ended questions. An open-ended question is one that requires elaboration and details to answer properly. A closed-ended question is one that requires a simple binary response such as yes or no. Because an interview is a very focused conversation, proper use of open- and closed-ended questions can help us be economical with our time and words. Closed-ended questions are good for establishing basic relationships. Here are some examples:

- "Is this your procedure?"
- "Have you ever had to tag nonconforming product here?"
- "Is this the current work order?"
- "Will you start a new batch this afternoon?"

Open-ended questions can't be answered with a yes or a no. They require the respondent to provide details. Audit interviews often start with closed-ended questions to establish basic relationship, and then move to open-ended questions to get deeper into the process. Here are examples of digging deeper with open-ended questions:

- "How do you know the engine was correctly assembled?"
- "What is the process for mixing the ingredients?"
- "How do you inspect the set-up?"
- "Why is necessary to install the flange before tightening the screws?"

When we believe there could be a nonconformity, we can return to the closed-ended questions to confirm the details:

- To confirm the requirement: "Do you agree that the procedure requires you to have a job ticket before starting work?
- To confirm the evidence: "Do you agree that this particular job was started without a job ticket?"

Note: This line of questioning could be viewed as condescending and would typically only be used if there was a disagreement about the presence of a nonconformity.

Silence is another technique that is sometimes used during interviews. I have seen auditors promote silence as a type of pressure tactic to force additional information. Audits are not games of manipulation, though. I would never promote silence as a tactic for introducing pressure or anxiety into the interview. Silence is really nothing more than a courtesy to allow the auditee to fully develop their response. When you ask the employee a question, you might need to wait a few seconds while he or she thinks about the answer. Inexperienced auditors are frequently uncomfortable with silence, and they'll often try to fill this gap with another question. Silence is a natural part of the ebb and flow of a conversation. Some audit interviews will be dynamic exchanges of information in rapid fire, while others may have brief periods of silence. Focus on making the auditee comfortable and you will always have a successful interview.

FREQUENTLY ASKED QUESTIONS

We have an auditor who spends all of her time during the audit examining records. She's very uncomfortable talking to employees. What should we do about this?

Remind her that the audit is a balanced examination of evidence. Records are part of it, but interviewing is also required. Then pair her with an auditor who has strong interpersonal skills so they can both learn from each other.

Some of our employees literally hide during the audit for fear of being interviewed. How should we handle this?

Their managers need to explain that the audit is not about them. The purpose is to improve processes, not to get anybody in trouble. All employees should be excited about being audited so they can demonstrate how much they know.

We interview employees in our conference room because it's a comfortable and quiet environment to talk in. Is this OK?

Probably not. Employees should be interviewed in their actual work environments. This will provide a realistic context for the conversation and make it easier to access other evidence such as records.

Chapter 9

Writing Nonconformities

T he term "nonconformity" inspires fear in many people. It shouldn't. A nonconformity is simply an opportunity for the management system to improve. It shouldn't be viewed as an indictment of any person or group, but rather as a factual statement that drives improvement. Before we go any further, it's helpful to provide a clear definition of what a nonconformity is:

A nonconformity is the failure to meet a requirement.

It's a short definition, but it packs a lot of power. Notice the word "requirement." You need a requirement before you can have a nonconformity. When writing a nonconformity, you always state the requirement first. It sets the tone for everything else. You can't have a nonconformity if you can't find a corresponding requirement. You might have a concern, observation, remark, or opportunity for improvement, but it's not a nonconformity unless it's clearly tied to a requirement.

The second half of a nonconformity is the objective evidence. The evidence states exactly what the auditor saw, heard, read, or experienced that contradicted the requirement. The objective evidence is factual and traceable, but it's stated as concisely as possible. A good auditor simply cites the evidence that fails to meet the requirement.

A child could write a clear nonconformity. It's a simple one-two process.

- *Requirement:* The company committed itself to doing XYZ. The commitment is a fact evidenced by its presence in a procedure, plan, policy, specification, contract, work instruction, standard, or statement.

- *Evidence:* The company failed to do XYZ. The failure is a fact based on evidence such as records, observations, documents, or interviews.

There should be no opinion in a nonconformity, just cold, hard facts. It's hard to argue with facts. It also makes the audit go much smoother. Sure, facts may remove a degree of creativity, but creativity is better expressed in other ways.

Writing effective nonconformities is one of the most fundamental auditing skills. Despite its fundamental nature, it's a skill that even the most experienced auditors struggle with. Here are a few keys to help you write nonconformities:

- *Match the requirement with concise evidence.* This is the single most important key. State the requirement, then provide the evidence that shows that the requirement wasn't met.
- *Write in complete sentences.* Your 8th grade English teacher insisted that you write in complete sentences and so does good auditing practice. Complete sentences, in both the requirement and the evidence, provides the customer of the audit with a complete product. This complete product is more likely to be understood and more likely to be acted upon.
- *Include all applicable identifiers (who, what, when, where).* It's critical that your evidence is fully traceable. Include all identifiers: what the nonconformity was, who was involved, when it happened, where was it located, and how much was involved. This builds credibility in the evidence and allows the auditee to know exactly what needs to be done to remedy the situation. The only identifier not clearly stated are people's names. We use job titles in the evidence because we want to remind everybody involved that the audit is about the process, not people.
- *Use an economy of words.* Writing a nonconformity is a balancing act. It needs to include all identifiers, but it also needs to be brief. As Shakespeare wrote, "Brevity is the soul of wit." Not only is brevity the soul of wit, but it helps drive understanding. Ironically, including more words rarely increases anybody's understanding of what you're trying to communicate. Keep your nonconformity statement nice and tight. If you can remove a few words while still communicating the essential message, then by all means do it.

- *State the facts, not your opinions.* The audit is about facts, not editorializing. This happens when the auditor tries to explain why the nonconformity is harmful or what the effects could be. This isn't necessary. Just state the evidence and no more.

Here is an example of a well-written nonconformity:

Requirement: SOP #QOP-32, revision 3, states in section 6.5 that employees must wear white gloves when handling finished product. State where the requirement comes from. In this case, it's a procedure written by the organization being audited. Provide the procedure number, revision, and even the section. Some auditors also include the procedure name, which can also add value. Once the requirement's origin is identified, state what the requirement is. Don't paraphrase it or get creative, repeat the requirement word for word.

Evidence: The auditor observed two employees in the warehouse handling finished product without white gloves. The language in the evidence mimics the language in the requirement. The organization committed to wearing white gloves when handling finished product, but the auditor observed two people not wearing them.

Here is an example of a poorly written nonconformity:

Requirement: All products must be identified. There is no traceability to this requirement. Where did it come from? There is a similar requirement in ISO 9001:2015, but it isn't referenced. Always cite where the requirement is coming from, and never paraphrase it. It's permissible to add ellipses if the requirements are taken from a long passage and the entire section isn't needed.

Evidence: Returned goods were missing the nonconforming materials tags, which greatly increases the chance of accidentally shipping bad material. This evidence has a lot of problems, most of which can be summarized by saying the evidence is not traceable. First, there's no indication of where the returned goods were located. The returned goods aren't uniquely identified in terms of their descriptions or part numbers. The quantity of returned goods isn't indicated; there could be two or 200. It's not clear. Finally, the auditor included a lot of editorial opinion at the end of the evidence. This only serves to inflame the auditee. Stick to the facts when you write evidence and make sure the facts are fully traceable.

HOLDING AUDITORS TO A HIGHER STANDARD

It's tempting to just say "Who cares?" when it comes to writing clear and correct nonconformity statements. After all, the rest of the world writes very informally. Grammar, correct spelling, and proper usage all seem optional these days. As long as the auditee understands what I'm talking about, it's OK, right? No, it's not OK.

Auditors must produce a polished and professional product. Everything you write, say, and do will be scrutinized by the auditee. This isn't to disparage you, but to ensure that the audit is credible. The output of the audit that gets the most attention are nonconformities. Although nonconformities aren't directed at any particular person, auditees are still keenly aware that they represent failings of a sort: A requirement was established, but it wasn't met. Because of the high profile of nonconformities, they need to be written very well.

If you're auditing with another person or as part of a team, have a team member review your nonconformity statements. This is usually the role of the lead auditor, but any set of trained eyes are helpful. The auditor who originally wrote the nonconformity should rewrite the nonconformity if necessary. Recognize also that sometimes the answer isn't reworking the nonconformity, it's ripping it up. The following conditions usually result in a nonconformity being removed from the final report:

- Requirement doesn't actually exist.
- Requirement is outside the scope of the audit.
- Evidence isn't traceable and it's too late to gather the details.
- Evidence relies on hearsay, rumors, second-, or third-hand information.
- Auditee presents evidence after the original interview that shows the requirement was met.

This is a good time to address findings that fall outside the scope of the audit. They could be in a department or process that isn't officially a part of the audit or against a standard that's not part of the audit. For instance, something happening in the warehouse constitutes a nonconformity, but the warehouse isn't part of the audit. Or the auditors observe a safety violation, but the audit is against ISO 9001 and safety isn't included.

Consider verbally reporting the finding to your contact within the auditee organization if you're faced with these kinds of situations. Mention that it's outside the audit scope and ask your contact if he or she would like you to include it in the report. If the answer is "no," then don't include it. The scope of the audit is almost a contract, and you don't intentionally audit outside the scope or report findings that are outside the scope. It's perfectly fine to make a note of the issue and follow up the next time there is an audit that includes that topic.

TREATING THE AUDIT AS A "GOTCHA" EXERCISE

Remember, the objective of the audit is to find out where the organization *is* meeting requirements. You'll likely find instances of the organization failing to meet requirements. It's all part of the improvement process. However, finding nonconformities isn't the purpose of the audit. The purpose is to evaluate conformity and to identify opportunities for improvement.

Treating the audit as a "gotcha" exercise is a trap that inexperienced auditors often fall into. After all, it's satisfying to identify a nonconformity. You were perceptive and observant, and this makes you feel good. This satisfaction can sometimes turn into outright glee with nonconformities. Of course, this behavior tells that auditee that you're playing on the opposing team. You're not a partner in improvement; you're an adversary. People will stop trusting the audit process and your support will deteriorate.

Here are some "gotcha" techniques to avoid at all costs.

- *Keep digging until you find a problem.* Instead, remind yourself that the audit is only a sample, and some samples reveal no nonconformities.
- *Express satisfaction at identifying nonconformities.* There should be no satisfaction in finding nonconformities. An auditor is nothing more than a fact finder. Negative facts are no better than positive facts. You react the same to both.

- *Nitpick minor issues.* Don't focus on small or inconsequential issues. Ask yourself, "Will this issue help the auditee survive and improve?" If the answer is no, you might want to move on.
- *Fail to see the big picture.* The best auditors can see the big picture of the auditee's competitive environment. They focus on issues that affect customers and long-term success. The only way to do this is by preparing before the audit and truly understanding the world that the auditee exists within.
- *Intimidate people until they admit fault.* Some auditors believe that being a little scary will knock auditees out of their comfort zone, and here they won't be able to hide the truth. Being scary or intimating will only make people hate auditing. You will always get the most cooperation by being friendly and engaging.

OPINIONS

Everybody has opinions, including auditors. As people become wiser and more experienced, they tend to develop even more opinions. Many experienced auditors consider themselves to be especially wise and experienced, meaning they have loads of opinions. Sometimes these opinions become the basis for nonconformities, which is a huge mistake. Facts are the only legitimate basis for nonconformities. Opinions have no role in the process.

When you hear words like these, you know that you're using opinions:
- "What you really should be doing is… "
- "Consider these best practices."
- "Here's a neat idea you should adopt."
- "I encourage you to try these world-class methods."
- "What we used to do at my old company."

If the organization has formally committed to any of these, then they are fair game during the audit. More often, though, these are inventions originating from the mind of the auditor. Use your brain during the audit, but leave your opinions out of nonconformity statements.

One of the great ironies of auditing is that the more experience you have, the more likely you are to audit against opinions. Because you've seen a lot of good examples of how to do things, you begin to think you know the best way to do everything. You may unconsciously substitute these opinions for requirements. The best way to guard against the tendency is to only use traceable, verifiable requirements.

SURPRISES, ANYBODY?

Here's a news flash for you: Nobody likes surprises. The world provides too many of these already, so don't introduce more surprises during your audit. If you think you have a nonconformity, begin talking about it immediately. Make sure you have all the facts straight. It's common for an auditor to think he or she has a nonconformity only to have misinterpreted something. It's embarrassing to be in a closing meeting and discover that your precious nonconformity was actually a misunderstanding.

Inexperienced auditors sometimes think that they will make a bigger statement by holding surprises until the end of the audit. This will make a statement, but it will be a negative one. Surprises of this sort won't make people welcome the audit and they won't motivate people to improve. On the other hand, surprises will strongly motivate people to create obstacles to auditing. The essential point is that communication is your best friend during the audit. Communicate frequently and fluidly, and leave the surprises to somebody else.

When you think you have a nonconformity, perform these key steps:

- *Confirm the requirement.* Make sure you correctly interpreted the requirement. This is especially important for requirements written by the organization in its procedures and policies.
- *Confirm the evidence.* Evidence is what you see that either meets or contradicts the auditee's requirements. Ensure that you accurately understand the evidence and that the auditee has the same understanding.
- *Get agreement that there might be an opportunity.* Get the agreement from the auditee on the facts as you see them. Break the situation down into its component parts—requirement and evidence—and get agreement on both.
- *Take accurate notes of the details.* When you're gathering evidence during an audit, you have one chance to get the information. It's very hard to

recreate details after you leave an area. This means you must take accurate notes during the audit. Capture all facts about what you've seen or heard, and you'll have a much easier time writing the audit report.

OFFERING SOLUTIONS

The best solutions come from the auditee not the auditor. This is one of the hardest things to remember, but it's a universal truth. When auditees develop their own solutions, they're committed to them. It also gets people in the habit of thinking critically and engaging their brains. You want to do everything possible to encourage ownership in solutions and improvements. The minute an auditor proposes a solution, the auditor assumes ownership for the idea.

You will inevitably be asked the following questions during an audit:

- What do you suggest I do?
- How can we fix this problem?
- Can you recommend an improvement?

People are busy and would like to take the shortest path to compliance possible. If the auditee can get a pre-packaged solution, it's much easier than having to invent one. The result of this approach is that the auditee has limited ownership in the solution. When faced with these questions, remind the auditee that he or she is the process expert. The auditee knows vastly more about the process than you ever could as an auditor. Tell him or her to take some time and think about the range of options. If you need to educate the auditee on the intent or meaning of a requirement, then do so. But avoid suggesting improvements or solutions. That's the auditee's job.

EXPLAINING NONCONFORMITIES

As an auditor, one of your main jobs is customer service. If the auditee wants you to explain a nonconformity, of course you're going to do it. But if you must explain your nonconformities, you probably didn't write them as clearly and as concisely as possible. The definition of a nonconformity is: *Failure to meet a requirement.* This means that everything starts with the requirement, and the evidence that you cite must directly relate to the requirement. If you did this correctly, your nonconformity should speak for itself. Strive for this kind of simplicity and clarity. When you write nonconformities, imagine that your customer is a 10-year-old child. Write on that level. You will write more effectively and your auditee will always understand you.

NOT QUITE A NONCONFORMITY

Some organizations also include another category of finding called concerns, observations, remarks, comments, opportunities, recommendations, or any number of other names. These fall into a gray area that doesn't quite constitute nonconformity, but are still worthy of investigation. Sometimes these will include specific recommendations for acting based on past experience, established best practices, or regulatory requirements. These types of findings give auditors a chance to express opinions.

Audits are a great place for benchmarking and sharing best practices, if all parties to the audit understand and agree to how this will happen. Most audit reports will include a section for concerns or observations, and it's best to simply list these. Because they aren't technically nonconformities, there is no reason to include a requirement.

FREQUENTLY ASKED QUESTIONS

If we don't use the requirement/finding format of writing nonconformities, will our registrar write a nonconformity against our audit process?

No, not unless you included this as an internal requirement within your audit procedure. There's no ISO 9001:2015 requirement for using this format.

FREQUENTLY ASKED QUESTIONS

Our top management believes that auditors should suggest solutions when they write audit nonconformities. What should we do about this?

Diplomatically educate top management that the process owner has the responsibility for addressing nonconformities. Suggesting solutions takes away part of that responsibility.

Managers in our company try to fix nonconformities before the audit is even finished. Is this a good idea?

No. Being in a hurry to fix nonconformities usually results in simplistic solutions that don't address the true causes of a problem. Tell your managers to relax and take their time investigating nonconformities after the audit is finished.

We have some managers who like to argue about nonconformities. How should this be handled?

First of all, remain calm and collected. Get agreement on the two parts of the nonconformity: the requirement and the evidence. Discussing the nonconformity in its two component pieces helps people better understand the issue.

Chapter 10

Audit Planning

A udits don't create improvements by accident. They take a great deal of planning and coordination. I've often said that a well-planned audit almost runs itself, but a poorly planned audit runs itself into the ground. Audit planning is often neglected, so it's important to have a disciplined approach to planning.

Audit planning involves a significant amount of dialogue between the auditors and auditees. It's a dynamic process that begins well in advance of the audit itself. Planning typically happens in three basic phases:

1. Determining audit scope
2. Researching the organization to be audited
3. Developing an audit plan

DETERMINING THE AUDIT SCOPE

Nothing can happen until we know the audit scope. The audit scope is the boundary of the audit, usually expressed as departments or processes within the organization. It's sometimes also expressed as sections of a standard, such as ISO 9001. The scope is important because it serves almost as a contract between the auditors and auditees in terms of what can be included in the audit. The auditee agrees to provide evidence within the audit scope, and the auditor agrees to audit within the bounds of the scope. Having a clearly defined audit scope helps maintain a spirit of partnership during the audit.

The organization's audit schedule will typically provide guidance on what the scope of the audit is. In the audit schedule example presented earlier in the book, the schedule was divided by month. Referencing the current month would indicate the scope of the audit to be performed. The only detail that's sometimes not included on an audit schedule are the specific dates of the audit. The auditors and the audit client simply agree on the dates.

An audit scope can be very narrow or very broad. An example of a narrow audit scope could be, "The spare parts stock room at ACME Corp.'s Spartanburg facility." A much broader audit scope might be, "All processes and departments at ACME Corp.'s Spartanburg facility." The first audit scope might take an hour or two to fulfill, while the second scope would take multiple days.

The breadth of an audit scope usually depends on the time and resources available to perform the audit. It's common for internal audits to occur over periods of two to four hours. Given this allotted time, an audit scope would generally need to be no more than two departments. Through experience, auditors learn how much time they need to audit different parts of an organization.

RESEARCHING THE ORGANIZATION

Before you can do meaningful planning for an audit, you need to understand the organization you'll be auditing. If you're an internal auditor, you probably already know a number of essential details: key products, major processes, and company policies, for example. You should confirm the details required to develop an effective audit plan. Not only does this provide essential information, but it also opens friendly dialogue before the audit. The more dialogue you can have before the audit, the less anxiety and tension that will result. Here are details that you will confirm during your audit planning phase:

- How many employees are within the audit scope? This will influence the size of your sample when speaking to employees.
- What's the primary language spoken? Depending on the language, you may need to arrange for a translator.

- Are there multiple buildings? If so, how far are they from each other? This could influence travel time that must be factored into your audit plan.
- What are the work starting and stop times? What times are lunch and breaks? You will need to know these so you can align your audit plan.
- What are the primary raw materials for the process being audited? Where do they come from?
- What are the primary products of the process being audited? Who are the customers? How are the products used?
- Is any personal protective equipment needed? If so, who will provide it?
- Are any areas of the facility off limits? If off-limits areas are within the audit scope, how will the audit team gather evidence?
- Do any statutory or regulatory issues apply to the organization's products? If so, what are they?
- Who will act as guides for the audit team(s)?
- Does the facility have multiple work shifts? When do they start and stop? How will the audit plan take these into consideration?
- What are the key risks within the audit scope?
- Is document control centralized in the facility or managed in each department?
- Is records control centralized in the facility or managed in each department?
- Is corrective action centralized in the facility or managed in each department?
- Is training centralized in the facility or managed in each department?
- Is calibration centralized in the facility or managed in each department?
- Has the organization had any significant nonconformities or customer complaints recently?
- Do visitors require any kind of training or orientation before entering the facility? If so, how long will it require?
- Are any requirements of the standard (such as ISO 9001) excluded from the management system?

The final step of research is to request documents. You can't ask for everything. You don't have time to read every document, and they wouldn't all make sense to you anyway. However, there are certain key documents that you should request, including:

- *Quality manual (if one exists).* This will provide a general overview of the organization and references to lower-level documents. ISO 9001:2015 doesn't require a quality manual but many organizations have one anyway. It can be a source of valuable high-level guidance for auditors.

- *Organizational chart.* Seeing the reporting relationships of all personnel will help put the organization into perspective.

- *Policy.* Depending on the type of audit, this could be a quality policy, environmental policy, occupational health and safety policy, or any number of others. It's the highest-level document in the entire system, setting a philosophical tone for everything else.

- *Objectives.* These are the organization's measurable goals. Auditors benefit from knowing them in advance and incorporating the knowledge into their audit strategy.

- *Production control procedure (if it exists).* The name "production control" is simply a placeholder. What I am referring to will certainly be named something else. Ask your contact at the organization if it has any high-level procedures that describe the work of the department. This document will help to you understand the organization's work and controls.

- *Document control procedure and record control procedure (if they exist).* One of the most fundamental of quality control disciplines, the control of documented information will influence nearly every aspect of the audit. It's a universal topic that touches every department and process.

- *Management review procedure (if one exists).* Management review might be the most important process in the entire organization. Auditors should understand how it's performed before they even step foot into the company.

- *Training procedure (if one exists).* Many organizations don't have procedures for their training and competency process, but others do. The required training can be verified at every stage of the audit.

- *Purchasing procedure (if one exists).* This is another of the key support procedures that helps define the controls the organization has put into place.

- *Internal audit procedure (if one exists).* Internal auditors need to know this procedure because it's their job to follow it. This is one of the key procedures that should always be referenced by auditors at all stages of the process.

- *Control of nonconforming product procedure (if one exists).* In a manufacturing environment, control of nonconforming products is a key discipline. Auditors should understand the methods of identifying, recording, and dispositioning these products.
- *Corrective action procedure (if one exists).* Another process that influences nearly everything in the organization and one of the key drivers of improvement.
- *Any other documents that your contact thinks might be helpful.* You can even ask the question, "Can you think of any additional documents that might help me prepare for the audit?" Doubtless, a few additional documents will turn up.

Everything listed above is a document of some sort. In other words, information that helps manage a process or guide decision making. I recommend that you wait to request records until after the audit starts. That's not always the case, but documents are what will help you most before the audit. Getting access to records will inevitably lead to auditing in advance, which is really bad form before the official start of the audit.

We'll discuss how you can use these documents in preparation of checklists in a later chapter.

DEVELOPING THE AUDIT PLAN

An audit plan is the detailed agenda for a single audit. This contrasts to an audit schedule, which shows a number of audits over an extended time frame. An audit plan is the primary coordination tool used by the audit team to guide its activities. It also communicates to the auditees what to expect during the audit.

Audits of two hours or less don't necessarily require a timed audit plan. Short audits usually have very narrow scopes, and there may not be much to gain from breaking a two-hour audit into even smaller parts.

Audit plans are essential for audits that last a half-day or longer. The audit plan shows the timing of all activities during the audit. Start and stop times are indicated for all activities, as well as the departments being audited. Meetings, breaks, lunches, and travel are also shown. The level of detail on an audit plan depends on the overall length of the audit. A full-day audit might be divided into 30-minute or hour-long blocks of time, while a half-day audit might be divided into 15- or 20-minute blocks of time.

The audit plan should be communicated in advance. This allows the auditee to understand what will happen and when, and for the audit team to understand its roles and responsibilities. The audit plan drives full transparency of the audit and contributes to open, fluid communications. There should be no surprises leading up to and during the audit.

The audit plan is subject to change. The lead auditor should be willing to shift audit activities around to accommodate the needs of the organization. Issues that might require changes to an audit plan include customer visits, rush orders, machine breakdowns, employee injuries, and unexpected absences. If you make reasonable accommodations for your auditees, you'll find them to be much more receptive to the audit process.

The audit plan should be reviewed in the opening meeting. You will send the audit plan to the auditee well in advance of the audit, but as a courtesy it's reviewed and discussed during the opening meeting before the audit begins.

An audit plan typically answers the following questions:

- *Date.* When will the audit take place?
- *Location.* What's the audit's location?
- *Scope.* What are the boundaries of the audit?
- *Objective.* What is the point of performing the audit?
- *Auditors* Who will perform the audit?
- *Areas to be audited.* What functions, departments, or processes will be evaluated during the audit? Sometimes this is clear from the scope, but often not.
- *Topics to be audited.* What subjects will be audited in the given departments? Should the auditee expect questions about document control or management commitment? This not only gives the auditee a heads-up, but it also helps guide the auditors.
- *Timing of the audit.* When exactly will each department be audited? When will the opening and closing meetings take place?

The audit plan may also address other issues, but the ones mentioned above are the most common. The purpose of the audit plan is two-fold: to help the auditors understand exactly what they'll be doing during the audit and to allow the auditees to know what to expect. It isn't uncommon for the auditee to propose changes to the audit plan, usually minor alterations in the timing ("Instead of auditing sales at 9 a.m., can you come at 10 a.m.?"). Changes of this sort are entirely reasonable and should be accommodated to the extent possible.

The audit plan should be documented as concisely as possible. The exact format is usually dictated by the magnitude of the audit. A plan for an audit of an hour or two could take the form of an e-mail. A plan for a full day or multiday audit will often take the form of a matrix that indicates hour-by-hour blocks of activities. Whatever the format, the plan should be communicated far enough in advance of the audit for all parties to digest it and understand its effect on operations.

Here are examples of two audit plans:

- *Half-day audit for Johnson Metal Fabricators.* This is a very simple audit plan that shows two auditors working independently in an audit limited to manufacturing operations. It doesn't include references to company procedures or ISO 9001 requirements. This type of audit plan might work for short, simple audits in which the auditors are very familiar with the processes being examined. The audit plan is shown in figure 10.1.

- *Two-day audit for CAS Nippon Co.* This is a full system audit of an entire company that employs 50 people. It uses one auditor over two days, touching every part of the organization. This audit plan includes references to the applicable procedure for each section of the audit, making it very clear what requirements should be referenced. A detailed plan like this is especially good for a highly documented company that relies on its own procedures for process control. The audit plan is shown in figure 10.2.

There are many different styles and formats for developing an audit plan. The key is choosing an approach the helps the auditor to perform the audit as effectively and efficiently as possible.

Figure 10.1   ISO 9001 Audit Plan

Johnson Metal Fabricators
April 1, 20XX

Scope: Cutting, bending, welding, machining, painting, and final inspection for the manufacturing of custom metal fabrications at Johnson Metal Fabricators (JMF) in Atlanta, Georgia

Criteria: ISO 9001:2015, the organization's documented management system, and applicable customer requirements

Objectives: Verify the intent, implementation, and effectiveness of the quality management system and to identify opportunities for improvement

Auditors:

Team 1	Team 2
Craig Cochran	Joe Miller

Time	Team 1	Team 2	Both
8:00–8:15 a.m.			Opening meeting
8:15–9:00 a.m.	Cutting	Bending	
9:00–9:45 a.m.	Welding	Machining	
9:45–10:30 a.m.	Painting	Final inspection	
10:30–11:30 a.m.			Auditor review meeting
11:30–12:00 noon			Closing meeting
12:00 noon			Adjourn

James St. Croix will act as the primary JMF contact, and personnel from applicable areas will be sampled on a random basis during the course of the audit. All issues arising from the audit will be held in strict confidence.

Figure 10.2	ISO 9001:2015 internal audit plan

CAS Nippon Company
June 30-July 1, 20XX
Audit performed by Craig Cochran

Scope: The manufacture, testing, and distribution of advanced polishing compounds and media at 200 Northside Parkway, Atlanta, GA

Criteria: ISO 9001:2015, QMS documentation, applicable regulatory requirements

Objectives: To verify the intent, implementation, and effectiveness of the ISO 9001:2008 quality management system, and to identify where improvements can be made.

Thursday, June 30

Start	End	Function/Element/Activity	Applicable procedure(s)
8:00 a.m.	8:15	Arrival and coordination	N/A
8:15	8:30	Opening Meeting	N/A
8:30	9:10	Top management and management review	SOP-M01-000, SOP-M01-001
9:10	9:30	Sales and marketing	SOP-M02-000
9:30	9:50	Product management	SOP-M07-000
9:50	10:20	Purchasing/materials management	SOP-S02-000, SOP-M05-004, SOP-S02-001, SOP-S02-002, SOP-S02-004, SOP-S02-003
10:20	10:50	Technical services	SOP-S03-000
10:50	11:20	Quality assurance	SOP-S05-000, SOP-M05-000, SOP-M06-000,
11:20	11:40	Finance and control	SOP-M03-000
11:40	12:00	IT	SOP-S06-000
12:00	1:00	Lunch	N/A
1:00	2:00	Product development/design and development	SOP-D01-000
2:00	2:30	Customer service	SOP-S04-000
2:30	2:50	Document and record control	SOP-M05-001, SOP-M05-002
2:50	3:10	Safety	SOP-S07-000
3:10	3:30	Training	SOP-M04-000, SOP-S01-000

Figure 10.2	ISO 9001:2015 internal audit plan

CAS Nippon Company
June 30-July 1, 20XX
Audit performed by Craig Cochran

Thursday, June 30

Start	End	Function/Element/Activity	Applicable procedure(s)
3:30	4:00	Corrective action, preventive action, and continuous improvement	SOP-M05-005, SOP-M06-000
4:00	4:30	Facility management	SOP-S08-000
4:30	...	Adjourn	

Friday, July 1

Start	End	Function/element/activity	Applicable procedure(s)
8:00 a.m.	8:15	Arrival and coordination	N/A
8:15	9:15	Receiving	
9:15	9:45	Gyrating	SOP-P01-000
9:45	10:15	Whisking	SOP-P02-000
10:15	10:45	Transplation and deposition	SOP-P03-000
10:45	11:15	Coating	SOP-P04-000
11:15	11:45	Cutting and finishing	SOP-P05-000
11:45	12:45	Lunch	N/A
12:45	1:30	Testing	SOP-P06-000
1:30	2:00	Configuration and packaging	SOP-P07-000, SOP-P08-000
2:00	2:30	Warehouse audits	SOP-P09-000
2:30	3:00	Shipping	SOP-S02-004
3:00	4:00	Auditor work time	N/A
4:00	4:30	**Closing Meeting**	N/A
4:30	...	Adjourn	

FREQUENTLY ASKED QUESTIONS

Our audits are only an hour or so in length. Do we still need an audit plan?

You certainly need to prepare for the audit, but you might not need a documented audit plan. In such a short audit, it would be difficult to divide up the audit activities into meaningful pieces.

I really don't have time to look at procedures and other documents before the audit. Can't I just read documents once the audit starts?

Sure, that's possible, but it's a bad use of your time. You'll bumble around without a clear audit path to follow. Ultimately, you'll get frustrated and so will your auditees. Do the preparation and you'll enjoy the audit and produce excellent results.

Is it possible to deviate from a published audit plan?

Yes, it's certainly possible. If you find that you must deviate from the audit plan, make sure that all stakeholders are notified. Also examine your audit planning process to see where it can be improved.

Chapter 11

Audit Checklists

A udit checklists are among the most useful tools to help audits run smoothly and stay on track. Auditors usually prepare checklists before the audit or they select appropriate checklists from a library of checklists the organization maintains. Having a checklist gives inexperienced auditors some confidence that they will not run out of questions or ask the wrong kind of question. Some of the best preparation an auditor can make prior to the audit is the development of a customized checklist. Most people think that auditors only use checklists during interviews, but they can be used anytime during the audit.

The beauty of a checklist is that it consolidates many important audit questions into one handy tool. A well-designed checklist keeps you from having to juggle around the ISO 9001 standard, company policies, departmental procedures, and work instructions all while you're trying to carry on a smooth conversation with the person you're auditing. Often, the process of developing or customizing a checklist imprints the questions on the auditor's brain, making them less reliant on the paper checklist.

Generic checklists can provide some general direction, but the value comes when the auditor customizes a checklist and adds specific requirements of the organization. These are some universal interview questions auditors can use in almost any situation. A good auditor will customize them with specific requirements from the organization he or she is auditing:

- *Please walk me through your process and what it requires.* This is nice way to start any employee interview. It puts the ball squarely in the employee's court and lets them lead you into the process. This one simple question can reveal a lot.

- *What do you need to start your job and where do you get it?* You're trying to get to the heart of inputs here. What supplies, materials, tools, and equipment does the employee need to do his or her job? Are they adequate and available when needed? How does the employee know the inputs are adequate?

- *Do you have any procedures or instructions that relate to your job?* If there are any standard operating procedures (SOPs), the employee should understand that they exist and be able to access them. The employee should also be following the instructions in the SOPs.

- *What kind of training have you received as part of your job?* The auditor should first understand the required training for that job. If the employee's answer differs significantly from the required training, then this issue will require further exploration.

- *How do you receive instructions on the product specifications and requirements?* The employee should have access to something that tells what the product requirements are. Compare the revision level on what the employee shows against the official revision level of the same document maintained by document control.

- *Do you use any measuring equipment?* If the employee uses measuring equipment, verify that it is fit for purpose and suitable for use.

- *What happens if you determine that the product or material is nonconforming?* This is a "what-if" question designed to test the management system's ability to deal with problems. Compare the answers you get against the company's procedure or requirements provided by supervision.

- *Do you perform any kind of inspections or tests on the product?* If the employee performs inspections or tests, he or she should clearly understand the criteria for pass versus fail. The employee should label any products that fail inspections or tests in accordance with the company's requirements.

- *Do you perform any kind of process monitoring?* If so, what happens if the process is operating outside of the specifications? Very often, organizations establish parameters for how a process must run. This could be speed, temperature, pressure, or a variety of other variables. If a process doesn't meet the requirements set for it, then correction must result.

- *How are inspection or test results recorded?* If the employee performs formal inspections or tests, he or she must record them in some way. Anything more than just a casual visual verification of the product is considered a "formal" inspection.
- *What risks apply to your job?* To be effective, employees need to have some understanding of the risks associated with their job. These can be risks to their health and safety, business risks to the customer, and operational risks to the organization itself. Just as important as understanding risks is comprehending what the organization is doing to manage the risks.
- *Are you responsible for any maintenance activities?* Many employees have some daily or weekly responsibilities for maintaining tools, machines, and equipment. These can range from simple checks of oil or hydraulic fluid to much more complex tasks. Auditors should verify that the required maintenance is taking place.
- *What measurable objectives relate to your job?* Employees don't need to memorize the objectives, but they should have a general understanding of what the objectives are.
- *How are you personally able to contribute to the achievement of objectives?* Employees should be able to come up with a few practical examples of how they can contribute to objectives during their normal activities.
- *In your own words, tell me what our quality policy means to you.* Employees should be able to provide a few key points from the policy in their own words. Being able to say how they contribute to some of the points in the policy would also suffice.

The questions listed above (which you will, of course, customize) would work well in a production process. In other words, an operational area where employees have specific responsibilities for carrying out services or manufacturing products. The questions exist simply as a bulleted list of items, with no overall structure. These questions and others are explained in further detail in chapter 16, "The Most Essential Audit Questions."

TURTLE DIAGRAMS

If you're someone who appreciates a bit more structure, then you might like the "turtle diagram" format for developing a checklist. This format incorporates all the typical elements of a process, including:

- Inputs
- Outputs
- Resources
- Responsibilities and authorities
- Methods
- Monitoring and measurement
- Risks
- Effectiveness

These process elements appear on the turtle diagram as placeholders. It's up to the auditor during his or her planning to populate these placeholders with specific requirements. For people who prefer a graphic touch to their documentation, the turtle diagram provides that benefit. Brevity is also a benefit, as a single diagram can represent an entire process.

In the days leading up to the audit, the auditor will use the organization's procedures, policies, instructions, and other resources to complete the turtle diagram template. The requirements can come from a wide range of sources, which the auditor consolidates onto the diagram. The finished product allows interpretation at a glance.

The small boxes that comprise the turtle diagram don't allow for much text. The requirements can't be reproduced in their original form as full descriptive sentences. They must be condensed into small snippets to fit. This demands that the auditor be familiar with the requirements; the auditor can't simply read them off a piece of paper. This limitation is a good thing. Nothing about the audit should be robotic, and a checklist of this sort helps reinforce the audit as a smooth and natural conversation.

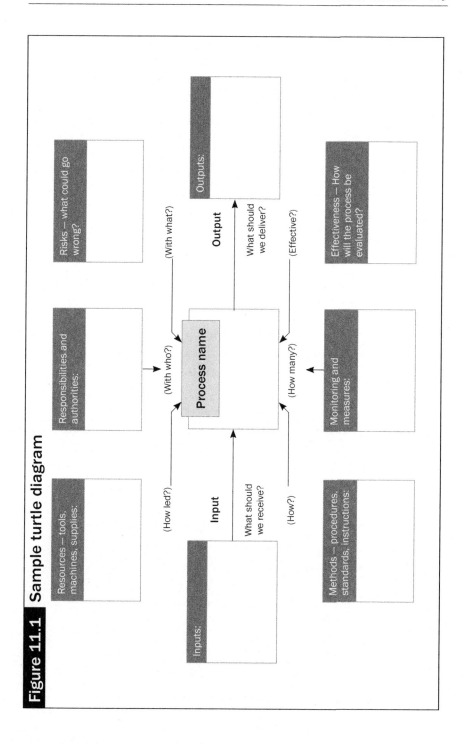

Figure 11.1 Sample turtle diagram

A completed turtle diagram for a shipping process appears in figure 11.2. As you can see, it's more of a memory prompt and still requires some knowledge of the process at hand. Every audit requires knowledge of the process, though. If the auditor isn't clear about a part of the turtle diagram, he or she can simply ask an employee about it. "Please tell me about the dock audits. When do they happen?" A quick glance at the diagram can keep the conversation flowing at a comfortable pace.

I use the turtle diagram as a notes page during my audit interviews, recording details in the margins and on the backside. As I've mentioned before, take your time and capture all the details. It's an awkward process to ask questions and write responses, but without actual evidence you haven't performed an audit.

LOOK AT/LOOK FOR

Another style of checklist that many people find helpful is the "Look at/ Look for" format. This style consists of two columns. The left column defines a type of evidence, such as a record, process, document, or person. The right column provides a list of requirements that the evidence must meet. The beauty of this format is that it gives you a number of requirements to check for every piece of evidence. As usual, it's the auditor's responsibility to create the checklist, drawing together as many sources of requirements as possible.

Let's say you're getting ready to audit a catering firm that provides lunches to small and medium-sized companies. When the catering company sets up each lunch, there are a number of requirements that must be met. The requirements come from a variety of sources: the firm's delivery procedure, set-up checklist, the standard contract, company policies, and statements made by the general manager. In your planning for the audit, you decide that observing a lunch set-up would be ideal. You confirm that this would be possible with the general manager of the catering firm, and then you set to work on your audit checklist. The "Look at/Look for" checklist for this process appears in figure 11.3.

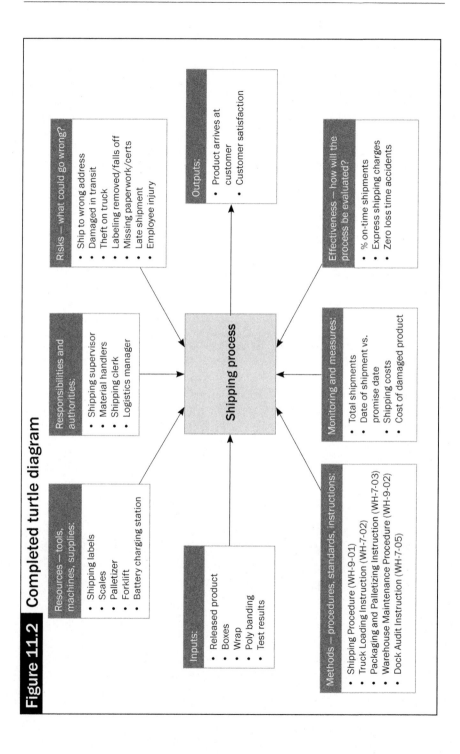

Figure 11.2 Completed turtle diagram

Resources — tools, machines, supplies:
- Shipping labels
- Scales
- Palletizer
- Forklift
- Battery charging station

Responsibilities and authorities:
- Shipping supervisor
- Material handlers
- Shipping clerk
- Logistics manager

Risks — what could go wrong?
- Ship to wrong address
- Damaged in transit
- Theft on truck
- Labeling removed/falls off
- Missing paperwork/certs
- Late shipment
- Employee injury

Inputs:
- Released product
- Boxes
- Wrap
- Poly banding
- Test results

Shipping process

Outputs:
- Product arrives at customer
- Customer satisfaction

Methods — procedures, standards, instructions:
- Shipping Procedure (WH-9-01)
- Truck Loading Instruction (WH-7-02)
- Packaging and Palletizing Instruction (WH-7-03)
- Warehouse Maintenance Procedure (WH-9-02)
- Dock Audit Instruction (WH-7-05)

Monitoring and measures:
- Total shipments
- Date of shipment vs. promise date
- Shipping costs
- Cost of damaged product

Effectiveness — how will the process be evaluated?
- % on-time shipments
- Express shipping charges
- Zero loss time accidents

Figure 11.3	Look at/look for	
Look at	Look for	Evidence
1 Lunch set-up at Apex Machine on 8-10-20xx.	Copy of contract signed by client (Set-up checklist, rev. 2, item 3)	
	Hot food served at the proper temperature: 145-150 F degrees. (Delivery procedure, Doc No. OP-07, rev. 1, section 2.1)	
	All trays covered (Set-up checklist, rev. 2, item 5)	
	Welcome sign and business cards on table (Hospitality policy dated 6-12-2016)	
	Plates, bowls, and cutlery on far-left side (Delivery procedure, Doc No. OP-07, rev. 1, section 2.1)	
	Flower bouquet in middle (statement by general manager)	

The "Look for" column includes the requirement to verify, along with the traceability of where the requirement came from inside the parenthesis. The "Look at/Look for" format doesn't have the graphic appeal of the turtle diagram, but it makes up for it by being so elementary that a child could use it. Another example of the same "Look at/Look for" checklist, now populated with evidence gathered during the audit, appears in figure 11.4.

As you can see, specific details of what the auditor observed are recorded in the Evidence column. There appears to be a nonconformity in the fourth row and a concern or observation in the final row. The next step after gathering evidence on the checklist is writing up formal findings. What would the nonconformity look like? Our formula for writing nonconformities is very simple:

- *Requirement:* Stated as simply as possible with traceability back to the source.
- *Evidence:* Written clearly and factually, with an economy of words. All identifiers provided.

Figure 11.4	Completed look at/look for checklist	
LOOK AT	**LOOK FOR**	**EVIDENCE**
1 Lunch set-up at Apex Machine on 8-10-20xx.	Copy of contract signed by client (Set-up checklist, rev. 2, item 3)	Contract signed by Don Stephens on 8-8-20xx. No changes or additional requirements noted.
	Hot food served at the proper temperature: 145-150 F degrees. (Delivery procedure, Doc. No. OP-07, rev. 1, section 2.1)	A thermometer was available in set up box. Auditor checked temperature of three hot trays and all measured within the tolerance.
	All trays covered (Set-up checklist, rev. 2, item 5)	All trays were covered with clear plastic wrap tucked under edges. Trays also had metal lids.
	Welcome sign and business cards on table (Hospitality policy dated 6-12-2016)	***Nonconformity: There were no welcome signs or business cards. The catering employee stated that the sign and cards were no longer used because they crowded the table.
	Plates, bowls, and cutlery on far-left side (Delivery procedure, Doc. No. OP-07, rev. 1, section 2.1)	All plates and utensils were available and organized.
	Flower bouquet in middle (statement by general manager)	Flower bouquet was in a small vase on the serving table. ***Note: Organic debris from bouquet had fallen onto one of the food trays.

Keeping our formula in mind, here's our nonconformity:

- *Requirement:* The hospitality policy dated 6-12-2016 states, "Welcome sign and business cards are to be placed on the table where food has been arranged."

- *Evidence:* At the lunch prepared for Apex Machine on 8-10-2016, the auditor observed that there was no welcome sign or business cards on the table where food had been arranged. The catering employee stated that the company no longer used the sign and cards because they crowded the table.

Take the time to develop a customized audit checklist for each organization you audit. The time and effort you spend on it will be an investment in effective results and result in a very smooth audit.

FREQUENTLY ASKED QUESTIONS

Does ISO 9001:2015 require that we use audit checklists?

No. ISO 9001 has never required the use of checklists, though checklists have obvious value in keeping the audit focused and efficient.

We use checklists, but we don't require our auditors to record evidence on them. Is that OK?

If your procedure requires that your auditors use checklists, then recording evidence on them would be the only way to prove that it happened. Recording details on a checklist can also aid in organizing audit notes. Ultimately, the decision is up to your organization.

We maintain a library of audit checklists on our computer server. Our auditors frequently download and revise them before auditing. Do we have to make a formal revision each time a checklist is changed?

No, that would be unmanageable. There would certainly be value in reviewing your checklists yearly to make formal revisions, though.

Chapter 12

Opening Meetings

Have you ever felt anxious about something that was about to happen? Imagine if the "thing" was called an audit. Your anxiety would be sky-high. The truth is that audits are always a little nerve wracking, no matter how much preparation and communication happens ahead of time. An opening meeting aims to remove this anxiety and sets the tone for a smooth, friendly audit that is focused on improving processes.

The name "opening meeting" is probably a little grandiose for what this really entails. We're talking about a short, usually informal meeting to go over the audit plan and discuss the basic details of the audit. For an internal audit, the opening meeting can take as little as five minutes. The auditors briefly go over the audit plan, line by line, and ask if any changes are needed. Questions about the audit are addressed. A friendly opening meeting gets the ball rolling toward a successful audit.

The opening meeting typically takes place in a conference room (for larger groups) or an office. Participants include the auditor(s) and the main auditee contact. I have led opening meetings with as few as two people and as many as 200 people. The exact size of the opening meeting is really up to the organization being audited. During your pre-audit communication, it's helpful to tell your organization contact that you'll be having an informal opening meeting prior to the start of the audit. You can add that the organization should feel welcome to invite whatever personnel it wants to, and that you'll be covering some basic details about the audit.

The lead auditor conducts the opening meeting. If there is a team taking part in the audit, there's not much for the other auditors to do or say. After all, the whole thing lasts a few minutes and provides an overview of the audit. The closing meeting will have many more opportunities for involvement by other auditors.

You may be wondering, why something that just lasts a few minutes is so important. The opening meeting does sound a bit inconsequential. It's not. The event may be simple but the outcomes are critical. Consider what results from the opening meeting:

- Comfort about the audit process
- Spirit of partnership in improvement
- Warm introduction to key participants (auditors and usually the managers of the areas being audited)
- Agreement on any scheduling changes
- Answering of questions
- Trust that the auditors are seeking conformity, not nonconformity

The opening meeting will be less important if the organization has been audited multiple times and is already comfortable with the process. It never gets skipped, though. You always start with an opening meeting to give the auditing process the dignity it deserves and cover what will happen once the auditing begins.

It's common for auditors to use a checklist to conduct the opening meeting. Here's a detailed explanation of each agenda item:

1. *Welcome.* Begin the opening meeting with a warm welcome to everybody present. A big smile and a friendly voice will help establish a tone of cooperative improvement. You may also want to let everybody know that the opening meeting won't last more than a few minutes. *"Thanks for coming to our opening meeting this morning. We're just going to cover a few details about today's audit and let everybody get on their way."*

2. *Introductions.* These may or may not be necessary, depending on everybody's familiarity. Make sure that nobody is a stranger. Knowing somebody is the first step toward trusting them. *"My name is Craig Cochran, and I'll be leading the audit. Dennis Kelly will be auditing with me. And*

this is the manager of the production area, Tim Israel. We appreciate you welcoming us to your department, Tim."

3. *Scope.* Describe the boundaries of the audit in terms of departments, functions, and/or processes. A clearly defined audit scope helps to remove confusion. *"The scope of today's audit will be the production area, which includes the molding, machining, and finishing processes."*

4. *Criteria.* Communicate the general requirements against which the audit will be conducted. This usually includes an outside standard (such as ISO 9001) and the organization's policies and procedures. There's no need to list specific procedures, unless the audit criteria are very narrow. *"We'll be auditing against ISO 9001:2015, your documented management system, and applicable customer requirements."*

5. *Objective.* Complete your introductory remarks by stating the objective of the audit. Possible objectives include preparing for ISO 9001 certification, addressing organizational weaknesses, identifying opportunities for improvement, and many others. Everything that happens in an organization should have a purpose, and an audit is no exception. *"The objective of today's audit is to prepare for our ISO 9001:2015 transition audit, as well as to identify opportunities for improvement."*

6. *Review the audit plan.* Now you get into the details of the audit plan. It's helpful to go over every angle to remove the potential for confusion. Here are the most common details:

   ✓ Duration of the audit. *"We'll begin the audit at 8:30 a.m. and continue until 11:00 a.m."*

   ✓ Departments and/or processes to be audited and times. *"Molding will be audited from 8:30 until 9:15, machining will be audited from 9:15 until 10:00, and finishing will be audited from 10:00 until 11:00."*

   ✓ Documents to be used during the audit. *"We'll be using departmental procedures, customer specifications, and ISO 9001's requirements during our audit."*

   ✓ Anticipated schedule for closing meeting. *"We're planning on having a closing meeting at 11:30 a.m. today. At that time, we'll go over all the findings and discuss next steps. Feel free to invite anybody you think would benefit from being there."*

7. *Sampling.* The audit will be a representative sampling of evidence, not a 100 percent inspection. This should be obvious to all participants, but it's important to declare this limitation before the audit begins. *"We will select a random and representative sampling of evidence during the audit, with the objective of producing a balanced picture of operations. There is no way we could possibly conduct a 100 percent inspection of everything happening here, but we believe our sample will provide an accurate snapshot of current operations."*

8. *Company rules.* Clearly state the auditors' intention to following all company rules and safety precautions. *"We know that ear plugs and safety glasses are required while in the production area, and have come equipped with these personal protection items. Also, we'll make sure to stay within the painted yellow lines that indicate pedestrian walkways. As you've indicated, we will also stay with our company guide at all times."*

9. *Confidentiality.* Make a general commitment to maintain confidentiality related to the evidence gathered and conclusions generated during the audit. *"Everything we see during the audit and all the evidence we gather will be held in strict confidence. We will not share it with any parties outside of your organization."*

10. *Confirm changes.* It's not uncommon for emergencies and unforeseen events to emerge right before an audit. These can range from employee injuries to visits from regulatory bodies to urgent customer orders. Make sure to confirm that the audit plan is OK as published. If not, what changes need to be made? Try to accommodate any changes within reason. In rare cases, an audit might even need to be rescheduled. *"Do we need to make any changes to our audit plan? Let me know and we'll talk about possible alternatives. We don't mind changes to the timing of any of our activities to suit your operations."*

11. *Questions.* In a gathering as relaxed as the opening meeting, questions are usually addressed as they come up. Explicitly ask for questions at this point, just in case anyone was waiting on a cue. *"Does anybody have any questions or comments? Please don't be shy. All your thoughts are very important to us."*

12. *Thanks again.* Conclude the opening meeting with one more thanks to all in attendance. Thank them for coming to the opening and for their

cooperation and assistance related to the audit. Thank you is something you can't say too much during an audit. *"Thanks again for having us here today and allowing us to audit. I look forward to making this a real win-win activity, because I expect that we will learn a lot from you."*

With a brief opening meeting, you've invested in the success of the audit. The plan for the audit has been discussed and agreed to, and a feeling of mutual trust has been established. Now you're ready for a successful audit.

Figure 12.1	Opening meeting checklist	
Topic	**Explanation**	**Addressed?**
WELCOME	General welcome of everyone to the opening meeting	☐
INTRODUCTIONS	Introduce the auditors to the organization's management, as appropriate	☐
SCOPE	The boundaries of the audit in terms of departments, functions, and/or processes	☐
CRITERIA	The requirements against which the audit will be conducted (e.g., ISO 9001 and documented management system)	☐
OBJECTIVE	The purpose of doing the audit (e.g., to identify opportunities for improvement)	☐
REVIEW AUDIT PLAN	Duration of audit	☐
	Departments and/or processes to be audited and times	☐
	Documents to be used during the audit	☐
	Anticipated schedule for closing meeting	☐
	Ask if there are any changes or conflicts related to the audit plan	
SAMPLING	The audit will be a representative sampling of evidence, not a 100 percent inspection	☐
COMPANY RULES	We intend to follow all company rules during the audit	☐
CONFIDENTIALITY	Everything we observe during the audit will be held in strict confidence	☐
CONFIRM CHANGES	Confirm any changes that were made to the audit plan	☐
THANKS AGAIN	Thanks in advance for your cooperation and assistance during the audit	☐

FREQUENTLY ASKED QUESTIONS

Our opening meetings consist of little more than saying, "We're here for the audit." Is that OK?

Yes. If your managers are comfortable with the audit process and already know the agenda, then the opening meeting can be very simple. Briefly review the plan, ask if any changes need to be made, and address any questions. This can all be done in five minutes or less.

Do we have to pass around a sign-in sheet during the opening meeting?

No. If your audit procedure requires that certain people attend the opening meeting, then a sign-in sheet would be the proof of that happening. If there are no internal requirements for attendance, then there is little value in having a sign-in sheet.

Chapter 13

Closing Meetings

The closing meeting is the first formal presentation of audit findings to the auditee management. It features a complete and balanced review of audit findings and helps management to gather an overall picture of organizational performance. Throughout the audit, the auditors have been communicating their findings and discussing observations, so nothing in the closing meeting should come as a surprise. The closing meeting is an opportunity to review all the findings in one place and answer questions. The closing meeting also gives the audit a dose of dignity and professionalism, which is always helpful.

Most closing meetings last anywhere from 15 minutes to an hour, depending on the scope of the audit and the number of findings identified. The lead auditor conducts the meeting with support from the other auditors on the team. In addition to auditors, the closing meeting is attended by the management of the processes that were audited. The exact number of attendees is up to auditee management. There are nearly always more attendees at the closing meeting than at the opening meeting, simply because there are audit findings to discuss.

A closing meeting has many purposes, including:

- *Present audit findings to management.* Each nonconformity and positive finding is read exactly the way it was written. The auditors who wrote the findings generally read them, as opposed to having a lead auditor present all the findings. It's also very helpful for the auditors to hand out typed versions of the audit findings to meeting participants. This allows auditees to hear and read the results, ensuring there are no miscommunications.

- *Provide opportunity for questions and dialogue.* If the auditors have written the nonconformities correctly and there has been adequate communication during the audit, there probably won't be many questions. Auditors must always remember that they are in the business of customer service. Make sure to answer any questions clearly and completely. The only questions that auditors generally don't answer are the right ways to address nonconformities. That's left up to the auditee. When an auditor proposes specific solutions and actions, he or she has effectively taken ownership of the improvement effort. That should remain with the process owners.

- *Agree on next steps.* The most obvious next step is for the auditee to take corrective action. The auditors will communicate their role (if any) in the corrective action process, and the auditee management will generally commit to a date by which they will have investigated and proposed action on the nonconformities. It's always a good idea for auditors to remind auditee management that all nonconformities should be matched with a corrective action.

- *The final purpose of the closing meeting is intangible: building credibility in the audit process.* You should conduct the closing meeting in a polished and professional manner that communicates to all involved that this is a serious improvement process. Consider using a checklist to make the closing meeting go smoothly and efficiently. Some auditors also prepare a visual presentation for closing meeting (using PowerPoint or similar software) to add some graphic appeal to the gathering.

The following list outlines the agenda items of a typical closing meeting. They follow the closing meeting checklist included and in many ways reflect the same items addressed in the opening meeting. The lead auditor generally covers the first few discussion points, with the findings being read by the auditors who wrote them.

1. *Welcome.* This is exactly what it sounds like, a hearty welcome to everyone who took the time to attend the closing meeting. It's very common to have far more attendees in the closing meeting than you had in

the opening meeting. The reason is obvious: You've got results to talk about. *"Welcome to the closing meeting for today's audit of the production area. We learned a great deal from you and were impressed by a lot of what we saw."*

2. *Thanks and introduction.* Having completed the audit, you have a lot to thank the auditees for. In all likelihood, they've been candid, cooperative, and hospitable, and you want them to know how much you appreciate their efforts. You will also re-introduce the auditors, as there are likely more people present in the closing meeting than there were in the opening meeting. *"Thanks for everybody's help during the audit. We couldn't have done it without you, and we want to extend a sincere thank you to all of you. There are a few people here who were not present during the opening meeting, so I'd like to reintroduce the audit team."*

3. *Scope and objectives.* Remind the attendees of the boundaries of the audit and the purpose for doing it. This will be very similar to what was said in the opening meeting. *"I'd like to remind everybody that the scope of today's audit was the production area, which included the molding, machining, and finishing processes. The objectives of today's audit were to prepare for the ISO 9001 surveillance audit by our accredited certification body and to identify opportunities for improvement."*

4. *Criteria of the audit.* Remind everyone of the audit criteria, which are simply the categories of requirements against which the audit was conducted. *"The criteria of our audit were the ISO 9001 standard, company QMS documentation, and applicable customer requirements."*

5. *Confidentiality and sampling.* Just as in the opening meeting, you will provide a commitment to confidentiality. You will also remind management that the audit consisted of a sample of processes, procedures, work areas, etc. *"Everything we saw today will be held in strict confidence, and we will not disclose our observations to any other parties. I'd also like to remind everybody that the audit was a sample, not 100 percent inspection. We believe that our sample was representative of the available evidence, but there is no way we could look at everything given the limited time on our audit plan."*

6. *Methods and documents used.* Provide a brief description of the audit process so management understands the overall approach and can have confidence that the audit was conducted in an organized way. *"We audited by*

department, following the audit plan that was sent in advance. The primary documents used during the audit were ISO 9001 and your departmental procedures and instructions."

7. *Positive findings.* Before you talk about nonconformities, it's helpful to address the good things that the company is doing. This gives the auditors credibility and clearly demonstrates a balanced approach to auditing. The individual auditors will generally read any positives that they identified. They will also answer questions and engage in discussion as necessary. *"I'd like to begin our discussion of the audit results by talking about the positives the audit team identified."*

8. *Nonconformities and concerns.* This is the part of the closing meeting that generates the most interest. Even though you've tried to discuss issues identified during the audit in real time, there will be people who haven't heard the nonconformities. If you made a summary chart or graph, direct everybody's attention to it. Read the individual nonconformities and concerns exactly as they were written. Answer questions and engage in discussion as necessary. *"I'd like to talk about the opportunities that we identified during the audit. These included nonconformities and concerns. Please remember that nonconformities should be addressed through formal corrective action. It's your decision as to if and how you will address the concerns."*

9. *Recommendations based on the audit purpose.* As a service to the auditee, you should summarize the audit results into a handful of key points. These are the big issues that management should focus on. *"Based on what we observed during the audit, I believe we will be ready for the ISO 9001:2015 certification audit by our certification body. We still have two months to go before the visit, so I believe we will be able to effectively address all the nonconformities. I believe the single biggest issue we need to address is completion of required training for office employees."*

10. *Corrective actions.* One of the most important points of the closing meeting is to match each nonconformity with a corrective action. Some auditees will initiate corrective actions on concerns or observations, but that's their decision. Establish a clear understanding of whose responsibility it is to enter corrective actions into the system and the timetable for responding. *"We are handing out corrective action forms right now to the*

responsible managers. We recommend that you investigate each of these and propose corrective action within the next two weeks. We will review your corrective action plans and provide feedback."

11. *Audit report schedule.* If your audit procedure requires the output of a formal report, let everyone know when it will be published. *"We plan to finish the formal audit report from this audit within the next two days. This report will be forwarded directly to the quality manager, who will then further distribute it within the company."*

12. *Questions and answers.* Auditors are in the business of customer service. Make sure to have a customer service mentality. The closing meeting is a great opportunity to answer questions, clarify details, and remove confusion. Take as much time as needed to address everybody's questions and concerns. *"Please feel free to ask any questions that you have. As you know, we've attempted to communicate throughout the entire audit, but we realize there may still be lingering questions or concerns. Every question and concern is important to us."*

13. *Thanks.* Conclude the closing meeting by thanking everyone again for their assistance and patience. No matter how well the audit was planned and executed, it was still an inconvenience. *"Thanks again for your cooperation and assistance during this internal audit. We know that the audit took time and effort on the part of everyone here, and we can't tell you how much we appreciate your assistance. It was a pleasure working with you, and we look forward to doing it again soon."*

PREPARING FOR THE CLOSING MEETING

At this point, we should back up and talk about how auditors get ready for the closing meeting. They do this through an audit team meeting that takes place immediately prior to the closing meeting. It typically requires anywhere from 30 minutes to a couple of hours, depending on the scope of the audit. The lead auditor manages the meeting and reviews the information. The purpose is to get ready for the closing meeting and present a coherent, unified message to the auditee.

The lead auditor will review each of the nonconformity statements, providing feedback to the auditors. If the lead auditor has trouble understanding any part of the nonconformity, it's a sure bet that the auditee will have a tough time understanding it too. The auditors who wrote the nonconformity statements should do any rework on nonconformity statements, not the lead auditor. It's also important to review positives in the audit team meeting to make sure there are no contradictory messages.

After hearing all the facts of the audit, the lead auditor will generate a conclusion statement that summarizes the audit into some concise trends. This gives the auditee a clear message about what they need to do moving forward. Each nonconformity statement and positive should be read in its entirety to the auditee during the closing meeting, but the complete conclusion statement helps to summarize this.

It might be helpful to depict the results of the audit in a chart or graph, depending on the number of nonconformities. A Pareto chart is especially useful to highlight areas for improvement. Charts of this sort only make sense if there are at least seven or eight nonconformities. Converting raw information into graphics always improves this kind of message.

Remember that the whole point of the audit team meeting is to prepare for the closing meeting. Discuss roles and responsibilities for the closing meeting and make sure that everybody understands his or her part.

Figure 13.1	Closing meeting checklist	
Topic	**Explanation**	**Addressed?**
WELCOME	General welcome of everyone to the closing meeting	
THANKS	Thank everyone for their assistance, hospitality, and candor during the audit	
INTRODUCTIONS	Introduce the auditors again, as appropriate	
SCOPE	The boundaries of the audit in terms of departments, functions, and/or processes	
CRITERIA	The standard against which the audit was conducted (e.g., ISO 9001) and documented management system	
OBJECTIVE	The purpose of doing the audit (e.g., to identify opportunities for improvement)	

Figure 13.1	Closing meeting checklist–continued	
Topic	**Explanation**	**Addressed?**
METHOD	How the audit was conducted (e.g.. We audited by departments using the plan sent in advance.)	
SAMPLING	The audit was a representative sampling of evidence, not a 100 percent inspection.	
POSITIVES	The best practices or highlights identified during the audit	
NONCONFORMITIES	1. Show graphic overview of NCs	
	2. Read each individual NC	
CONCLUSIONS / RECOMMENDATIONS	The conclusions that can be drawn, based on the purpose of the audit (e.g., the organization is nearing readiness for ISO 9001 certification, but needs to focus on the following areas...)	
CORRECTIVE ACTIONS	The date by which corrective actions should be investigated and the person they should be returned to	
REPORT	The date the report will be completed and who it will be sent to	
CONFIDENTIALITY	Everything observed during the audit will be held in strict confidence	
QUESTIONS	Does anybody have any questions or concerns about the results of the audit?	
THANKS AGAIN	Thank everyone again and say that you look forward to the chance of working with them again	
NOTE: If the nonconformities were categorized in terms of MAJOR and MINOR, then the criteria for these categories would need to be described prior to going over the nonconformities.		

Figure 13.2 — Sample closing meeting presentation

Audit of ACME Inc.
ISO 9001:2015

August 23-24, 2016
Craig Cochran & Don Pital
Georgia Institute of Technology

Positives

- Engagement & enthusiasm of all personnel
- Leadership & management involvement
- Communication
- Employee recognition
- Water deliveries to production

Positives

- Work-a-long process
- Lots of proactive customer feedback
- "Express yourself" program
- Key measures connected to ICM

Categories of audit findings

- Major nonconformity
- Minor nonconformity
- Concern

Audit findings

Section title/description	Classification			TOTAL NUMBER
	Major	Minor	Concern	
Document control	1	3	3	7
Preservation of product		1	1	2
Identification & Traceability		1	1	2
Calibration		1	1	2
Management review	1			1
Corrective action		1		1
Control of records		1		1
Maintenance			1	1
Training			1	1
Purchasing			1	1
Quality manual			1	1
TOTALS =	2	8	10	20

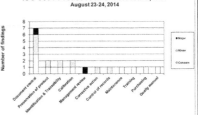

ISO 9001 Preassessment of ACME, Inc.
August 23-24, 2014

Conclusions

- ACME has an effective and impressive management system
- The facility is very close to ISO 9001:2015 conformance
- No "Big hairy issues"
- Biggest opportunity areas: Document control, management review, broader use of corrective actions

Thanks for everything!

- It has been a real pleasure working with the fine people of ACME
- Don't hesitate to contact us if we can assist further

FREQUENTLY ASKED QUESTIONS

Does the closing meeting have to include top management?

No, but if you can include top management it will underline the importance of auditing. Top management's presence will send a powerful message to the organization.

During the closing meeting, we require that the responsible managers sign each nonconformity statement. Is this necessary?

No, but if it helps create accountability, there might be value in it.

Because of the way we do audits over the course of a month, it doesn't make sense to conduct a closing meeting. Should we change this?

Yes. The closing meeting provides an opportunity to discuss audit findings and build a better understanding of the audit process. If the closing meeting is skipped, many managers will remain ignorant of auditing, its value, and their role in addressing nonconformities.

Chapter 14

Reporting

An audit report is a written summary of the audit results. It can range from less than a page to more than 10 pages, but for internal audits shorter is generally better. Long reports simply aren't read. Many aspects of the audit process are team activities, but it's best to have an individual write the audit report. This helps to create a unified and coherent overview of the audit.

The auditor usually submits the audit report after the closing meeting, though sometimes a report is provided during the closing meeting. Interest in the audit drops significantly for every day that passes after the closing meeting, so try to provide the report as quickly as possible. The report discusses the overall trends of the audit and provides some basic details about how the audit was conducted. It's common for companies to have very brief audit report forms to make the audit report as simple as possible.

ISO 9001:2015 doesn't explicitly require an audit report. The standard does require records of the results of audits. This could be achieved through a combination of records such as audit notes, audit plans, and corrective actions. The audit report pulls together a number of key details into one simple package. Here are the benefits of an audit report:

- Serves as the official record of the audit
- Provides a concise input to management review
- Facilitates analysis of trends
- Provides proof of the audit covering the entire scope
- Creates a record of positives identified during the audit

- Assists auditors in preparing for subsequent audits
- Aids in assigning resources for future audits
- Builds confidence in the audit process as a driver of improvement

There's no glory in writing a long, drawn-out report that nobody reads. A simple report form will provide the benefits of a report without the effort and time commitment that would be typically be required. Here are the key elements of a sample report form:

- *Date:* Date that the audit was performed.
- *Audit team members:* Persons performing the audit. If one of the auditors was designated as the lead, then this should be noted.
- *Areas/departments audited:* The scope or boundaries of the audit, stated as areas or departments of the company.
- *ISO 9001 elements:* The sections of ISO 9001 that were audited against.
- *Documents used:* The procedures, policies, and instructions used during the audit. A wide range of documents provides proof of fulfilling the scope of the audit.
- *Records examined:* Records are the historical artifacts that provide evidence that requirements were met. Listing a range of records indicates that the audit performed due diligence in seeking evidence and selecting samples.
- *Personnel interviewed:* Titles of people interviewed during the audit. This isn't recorded to punish or reprimand individuals. Personnel interviewed indicates that the audit was comprehensive in selecting a diversity of people for evidence gathering. Don't list the names of personnel, only their titles.
- *Areas for improvement:* Summarize the areas that most need improvement. You're doing this as a convenience to managers who may not take the time to read the individual nonconformity statements.
- *Positives identified:* This section provides a location to record all the positives identified during the audit.
- *Number of nonconformities:* Confirmed nonconformities expressed as a number. Don't add nonconformities not shared during the closing meeting.
- *Number of concerns:* Concerns or issues that don't constitute nonconformities, but do deserve further consideration in the opinion of the audi-

tor. Organizations may refer to these as concerns, observations, recommendations, or opportunities for improvement.

The content of an audit report is dependent on the needs of the organization. Despite this fact, the success factors related to reporting are universal:

- Provide the report as quickly as possible.
- Keep the report short and sweet.
- Include some information about audit trends to facilitate analysis.

FREQUENTLY ASKED QUESTIONS

We don't include nonconformity write-ups in our audit reports, because the write-ups are already on corrective action forms. Is this OK?

Sure. There's no requirement that the report include the individual nonconformities. Including them in the audit report can be helpful from a historical context, though.

Does the audit report have to be signed by the lead auditor?

There are no requirements for who signs an audit report. Signing it—and thus having traceability back to who wrote it—is a good idea.

Does the audit report have to include all the evidence that was collected during the audit?

No. That would be a very long report.

Chapter 15

Audit Follow-Up

T he last step in the audit process is also one of the most important: the follow-up on nonconformities. All corrective actions resulting from the audit must be followed up. The key to effectiveness is evidence. You are seeking objective, factual evidence that corrective actions were effective. This evidence should show clearly that the process has been changed and the work output improved. Ideally, the evidence should show that the customer has had positive results from the corrective action, and that management recognizes it.

STEP 1: CAUSES

The starting point of follow-up is the examination of causes identified during corrective action. In the perfect world, process owners would investigate nonconformities with a completely fresh set of eyes. Tired, worn-out paradigms about the causes of problems would be discarded, and investigation would drill well beneath the surface.

More commonly, though, investigation produces causes that are no more than a restatement of the problem or variations on the symptoms. Symptoms can be a starting point, but they can't be the ending point. Investigation should reveal the actions or inactions that caused the nonconformity. The following causes are superficial at best and should always be rejected:

- Failure to follow procedure
- Employee error

- Sloppy work
- Not paying attention
- Willful negligence
- Management oversight
- Absence of supervision
- Systematic failure
- Forgot training

These are ineffective causes because they only scratch the surface. They blame nonconformities on people instead of processes. Investigation can *begin* with symptomatic or people-centered causes, but it must extend beyond this shallow perspective.

If a process owner declares that the cause of a nonconformity was "employee error," the next question should be, "What caused our employee to make this error?" The underlying causes almost always involve the organization's methods, procedures, and policies. This is the realm of management. Shallow, symptomatic causes must be sent back for rework.

STEP 2: **PLANNED ACTIONS**

The second step of follow-up examines the actions taken on nonconformities. Effective corrective action always involves change. The work has been officially changed, and the change has caused a reduction or removal of the nonconformity in question. The following actions are rarely considered effective because they don't change anything:

- Held a meeting.
- Retrained personnel.
- Counseled employee.
- Reminded everyone about expectations.
- Warned employees.
- Verbal reprimand.
- Initiated disciplinary procedures.

Not only do these not change anything about the way work is done, but they also reinforce the flawed methods that are already in place. At least half of them also treat the audit nonconformity as a personnel issue. The implication is, "If we had a nonconformity, then somebody must have been at fault. Let's find and punish a culprit." This is exactly the opposite culture you're trying to establish with a quality management system.

Attempts to fix audit nonconformities should focus on changing processes, not people. A flawed process will produce poor results no matter how smart and hard-working the people.

STEP 3: IMPLEMENTATION

Even if the identified causes and proposed actions make sense, you still have the issue of implementation. It doesn't matter how brilliant your action plans are. They're worthless unless implemented. You must confirm that the corrective actions have been implemented from start to finish. For simple audit nonconformities, there might be one or two actions applied. For more complex nonconformities, the resulting corrective actions might involve many actions and improvements. All the actions must be completed. You don't take someone's word for it, you seek objective evidence of action taken.

Sustainability is a natural offshoot of implementation, and it refers to how the actions are sustained and reinforced within the organization. All actions must be formally incorporated into the processes. This includes training, communication, documentation, awareness, monitoring, and measurement. These sustainability elements by themselves don't achieve anything, but when paired with a changed process they create robust improvement.

STEP 4: IMPROVEMENT

After confirming the actions, look for evidence that the process output has improved. Yes, the organization acted, but what are the results? This is the ultimate test of corrective action. You can do everything else correctly, but if there's no improvement, the corrective action can't be considered effective. The type of improvement will obviously differ depending on the changes made to the process. If the process improved, it should be more efficient with less waste. If the product improved, it should have less variation and adhere closer to customer requirements. Evidence is the key. You're seeking evidence of lasting improvement.

Evidence usually takes the form of data or records. Another powerful form of evidence is your own observations. That's not to say that you can't accept verbal evidence, but records, data, and first-hand observations are certainly better. The exact amount of evidence depends on the magnitude of the original problem. Broader and more severe problems lead to more profound improvement, which in turn require more evidence to verify effectiveness. It's simply a matter of scale. The scale of verification must match the scale of the actions taken.

The timing of verification must also match the actions taken. Most corrective actions have target dates for completion. The process owners tasked with the corrective actions typically set these dates. Don't follow up on corrective actions prior to these dates. Some corrective actions may be ready for verification within a week of initiation, while others may require months before they can be followed up on.

The best person to perform audit follow-up is somebody independent of the corrective action. An especially good person to follow up on corrective actions is the auditor who wrote the original nonconformity. The auditor has knowledge of the original issues and will already understand the evidence that led to the nonconformity. It's hard to follow up on a corrective action if you're completely unfamiliar with the original issue.

Be honest and open about your perceptions when performing audit follow up. If you don't believe a corrective action has been effective, be clear about it. Explain to the process owner what has led you to that conclusion. Prepare to provide some guidance on how to perform effective corrective action. An auditor never takes ownership over a corrective action, but he or she can provide some assistance.

In summary, here are verification points for audit follow-up on nonconformities:

- *Have real causes been identified instead of just symptoms?* Investigation into causes always involves going beneath the surface of the problem. Causes should focus on the process, not on people.
- *Have actions been planned that directly address problem causes?* Taking action on symptoms is akin to putting a Band-Aid on a serious wound. It

does nothing to treat the underlying causes. The actions taken must get beyond the superficial symptoms and address the underlying causes of the problem, removing or significantly reducing them. The single biggest reason for problem-solving failure is action on symptoms instead of true causes.

- *Are the actions fully implemented?* Speak to the people responsible for planning and taking action. Have their plans been fully implemented? Are there steps pending? What obstacles exist? You can't verify effectiveness until actions have been completed.

- *Have procedures been revised or developed?* Improvements don't stick unless they are made the new norm. Make sure that all relevant documentation reflects the improved method.

- *Are employees knowledgeable about changes?* If a process has been improved, employees will typically know about it, especially if they're responsible for implementing the change. Speak to employees in the work area and see if they're familiar with changes and their roles in implementing them. Awareness of improved methods may come from formal training processes or informal communications. If formal training is used, records of training would be another type of evidence that could be verified.

- *Are products/outcomes improved?* This is the essential point: Have the products been improved? An improved process should ultimately lead to improved products. Is there evidence this has happened? What do records and data indicate? Hearsay and verbal evidence can't be used to prove that products have been improved.

- *Has measurement or monitoring been established?* The effectiveness of corrective action can't be known without ongoing measurement or monitoring. In these cases, have the controls been put in place? What do the measurements indicate? Do the data indicate the process has improved and stabilized?

- *What is the customer's perception of the improvement?* Perception is everything. Have customers noticed a change in the quality of goods or services? Keep in mind that these could be internal or external customers. Locate the applicable customers and get their perspective. If customers haven't noticed an improvement, corrective actions haven't been effective.

- *Has the problem re-occurred?* If the problem continues to occur, then the corrective action isn't effective. Only data and records can be used to prove a lack of recurrence.
- *Is top management aware of the corrective action?* Top management can't be aware of every corrective action in the organization, but they should be aware of the large ones and overall trends. Top management awareness would certainly help support a determination of full implementation and communication.

These verification points appear in the checklist provided in figure 15.1.

It's common to perform audit follow-up at the next audit. This approach certainly works, but it's important to carve out an adequate amount of time on the audit plan for follow-up. It could easily take at least 20 minutes or more to verify each corrective action. Being in a rush while performing follow up will guarantee a cursory, haphazard job.

Figure 15.1	Verify effectiveness		
Questions to ask when verifying corrective actions			
Question	Explanation	Y/N	Results
Did the actions address problem causes, instead of just symptoms?	The actions taken must get beyond the superficial symptoms and address the underlying causes of the problem, removing or significantly reducing them.		
Are the actions fully implemented?	Speak to the people responsible for planning and taking action. Have their plans been fully implemented? Are there steps that are pending? What obstacles exist? You can't verify corrective actions until they are fully carried out.		
Have procedures been revised or developed?	Improvements don't stick unless they are made the new norm. Make sure that all relevant documentation reflects the new methods put in place by the corrective action.		

Figure 15.1	Verify effectiveness–continued		
Questions to ask when verifying corrective actions			
Topic	**Explanation**	**Y/N**	**Results**
Are employees knowledgeable about changes?	If a process has been improved, employees will typically know about it, especially if they are responsible for implementing the change. Speak to employees in the work area and see if they're familiar with changes and their roles in implementing them.		
Are products/outcomes improved?	This is the bottom line: Have the products been improved? An improved process should ultimately lead to improved products. Is there evidence that this has happened? What do records indicate?		
Has measurement or monitoring been established?	The effectiveness of some corrective action can't be known without ongoing measurement or monitoring of the process. In these cases, have the controls been put in place? What do the measurements indicate? Does the data indicate the process has improved and stabilized at the new level?		
Does the customer have any awareness of the improvement?	Perceptions are everything. Have customers noticed a change in the quality of goods or services? Keep in mind that these could be internal or external customers. Locate the applicable customers and get their perspective.		
Has the problem reoccurred?	If the problem continues to re-occur at the same level as before, then the corrective action is not effective.		
Is top management aware of the improvement?	Top management isn't expected to be aware of every improvement in the organization, but they should be aware of the large ones and overall trends. Top management awareness would certainly help support a determination of full implementation and communication.		

FREQUENTLY ASKED QUESTIONS

Can the people who took corrective action also follow up on their own actions?

This would rarely be effective. Most people are not objective enough to pass judgment on their own corrective actions. Recruit someone completely independent of the process to perform follow up.

Should formal corrective action be taken on each audit nonconformity?

Yes. It's not good enough to simply correct the problem. A corrective action should be initiated on each audit nonconformity.

Do we have to retrain employees every time we improve a process?

Not necessarily. Your improvement is not sustainable unless you cement it in place somehow, though. Retraining is one way, communication is another way, and simply having employees read revised procedures is yet another way.

Does follow-up have to happen during a formal audit?

No. Organizations can follow up on audit nonconformities in whatever manner they deem appropriate.

Chapter 16

The Most Essential Audit Questions

T he heart of auditing is interviewing personnel. It produces an abundance of objective evidence, and it's also what makes auditing so much fun. After all, you're having a friendly conversation with people who can teach you something. What could be more fun than that? Nevertheless, interviewing can be intimidating to some auditors. You can't hide behind documents or records when you're interviewing. Your interpersonal skills (or lack thereof) are on full display.

The two biggest fears of new auditors are asking the wrong questions and running out of questions. That's why an audit checklist is one of the most practical tools imaginable. It will keep you on track and relaxed, and this will lead to you making the most of your interviews. Here are some questions that can form the core of any internal audit checklist.

1. CAN YOU WALK ME THROUGH YOUR PROCESS AND WHAT IT REQUIRES?

This is a simple open-ended request that can open all kinds of interesting audit trails. It puts the ball entirely in the court of the auditee. There are no wrong answers. The person you're speaking to simply needs to describe his or her process in whatever way is most comfortable. The "what it requires" part also touches on information and other resources used in the process. A simple question like this puts the auditee at ease and provides the auditor with an overview of the entire process. It's the natural springboard into more in-depth questions. This request can also be directed at nearly anybody in the organization at any level. It's especially helpful for production processes.

2. WHAT DO YOU NEED TO START YOUR WORK?

Here we are beginning to dig a little bit deeper. You're trying to uncover the activity trigger. It might be a work order, a verbal command, or the arrival of raw materials. The only requirement is that it be clear and accurate. Incoming raw materials and supplies should meet all requirements, and the employee should know what indicates conformity. In the case of information that begins the process, it should be approved, up to date, and unambiguous. The responses you get from employees should be compared to what you're told by managers. If you get drastically different responses for what begins the work, you might have a nonconformity.

3. HOW DO YOU CONTRIBUTE TO OBJECTIVES?

A significant requirement of ISO 9001 and every other international management system standard is that measurable objectives be established at relevant functions and levels. Arguably, an even more significant requirement is that personnel understand how they contribute to objectives. This requirement doesn't just apply to some personnel—it applies to everybody. All personnel must be able to communicate, in their own words, how they help move objectives in the right direction. It's conceivable that not all objectives apply to all personnel. In those cases, auditors would only expect personnel to understand the objectives that apply to them.

This is a significant question because it directly reflects on the organization's ability to communicate what matters most to its success. True comprehension of objectives means that people understand specifically what they can do to improve the organization. They know the significance of their roles and they are prepared to carry them out. This kind of knowledge creates strategic focus throughout the organization. Instead of just having a micro view of activities and tasks, personnel begin to understand how their jobs link to the larger mission of the organization.

It's worth mentioning that ISO 9001 uses the term "quality objectives." This is a term that has confused many people over the years. It has wrong implied that objectives must be focused only on traditional quality topics. Objectives can be focused on whatever topics the organization finds appropriate. Many organizations have gotten value out of applying objectives to finance, cost control, inventory turns, innovation, safety, environmental stewardship, product improvement, process variation, and many others. It's never the job of the auditor to decide if objectives are sufficiently quality oriented.

Closely related questions include:

- *Are objectives documented?* Objectives should be treated like any other document, with revision control, approval prior to issue, and no obsolete versions available.

- *Are objectives measurable?* Objectives should be trackable using actual data. Unmeasurable platitudes such as "To become world class" have little value.

- *Is progress being made against objectives? If not, why?* The organization should be able to describe progress toward achieving objectives. If progress has not been made, corrective actions should be in place to find out why.

- *Are objectives established at relevant functions and levels?* This is a strange way of asking if everybody has at least one objective. Relevant means you have a purpose and role within the organization, which is true of everybody employed. This means that everybody will have at least one objective, established at the departmental level, site level, or corporate level.

4. WHAT HAPPENS WHEN PRODUCT IS NONCONFORMING?

This question reflects on the organization's ability to deal with product problems in a systematic way. Control of nonconforming products is one of the most basic disciplines, and one which smart auditors always probe. Compare the answer to this question to the documented procedure and, more importantly, to the auditor's observations. Few other processes require as rigid adherence to procedure as control of nonconforming products. Simply put, there is no room for deviation. The reason is that problems relating to controlling nonconforming products almost always pose huge risks to the organization: added costs, wasted time, aggravated employees, angry customers, loss of competitive position. During an audit, find some actual examples of nonconforming products (if any exist) and follow-up with these questions:

- *Identification.* How are nonconforming products identified?
- *Location.* Where are they physically located?
- *Responsibilities.* What are the responsibilities and authorities related to dealing with nonconforming products?
- *Dispositions.* How do dispositions get determined and implemented?
- *Records.* What are the records of nonconforming products and actions taken on them?
- *Connection to corrective action.* What are the linkages to the corrective action process?

It's worth mentioning that control of nonconforming product applies to services just as much as it does to tangible goods. Reports, data, test results, and intellectual property (to name just a few service outputs) can all be considered nonconforming, and all the disciplines of this process apply.

Sometime during your auditing career it's inevitable that you will encounter nonconforming products that are unidentified. No tag, label, marking, location, box, cage, or anything else that would provide positive identification. When this happens, the most typical response from the auditee is, "Everybody can tell that's nonconforming. It's obvious." There is no such thing as obvious nonconforming product. If the product is nonconforming, it must be identified as nonconforming.

5. HOW DO YOU ACCESS PRODUCT REQUIREMENTS?

Everybody has a product of some sort. It may be a product that goes to an external customer or one that goes to the next process inside the organization. In all cases, though, personnel need to understand the product requirements. ISO 9001 specifically requires that product requirements be identified along four angles: 1) requirements stated by the customer, 2) requirements not stated by the customer but necessary for intended use, 3) statutory and legal requirements, 4) additional requirements determined by the organization. The standard additionally requires that information describing the product be available (i.e., documented.) Asking how personnel access product requirements is a huge audit question because when requirements are not accessible, big problems often result. Employees don't need to know product requirements by heart, but they should certainly be able to find the current versions of requirements and describe how they carry them out. Specific points of inquiry related to product requirements include:

- Are requirements complete?
- Are requirements current?
- How do they get reviewed?
- Do personnel understand them?

A common ailment in many organizations is the generation of unofficial product requirements. These usually take the form of personal notebooks and files. The motivation for these is honest enough: Put product requirements at points of use and make them convenient to access. The only problem is that personal notebooks and files are not controlled. If requirements change, there's no mechanism in place for revising them, so we end up with a ready-made system for creating nonconforming product. Not very effective for driving customer loyalty. Keep an eye out for these "bandit" customer requirements as you perform your audits.

6. HOW DO YOU CORRECT PROBLEMS?

There is no shortage of problems. The shortage is in the disciplined ways of correcting problems. When significant problems arise, organizations should initiate corrective action. The corrective action steps are not complex: Define the problem, identify the causes, act to remove or reduce the causes, and verify the fix actually worked. The genius is in satisfying each step before moving onto the next step. As an interview topic, auditors are primarily interested in knowing if employees know their role in corrective action. If the organization has a written procedure for corrective action, the responsibilities will be clearly spelled out and easily verified. The real magic of auditing corrective action comes from the examination of records, though. Here are some key questions related to corrective action:

- *Did the actions address problem causes, instead of just symptoms?* The actions taken must get beyond the superficial symptoms and address the underlying causes of the problem, removing or significantly reducing them.

- *Are the changes fully implemented?* Speak to the people responsible for planning and taking action. Have their plans been fully implemented? Are there pending steps? What obstacles exist?

- *Have procedures been revised or developed?* Improvements don't stick unless they are made the new norm. Make sure that all relevant documentation reflects the new methods put in place by the corrective action.

- *Are employees knowledgeable about changes?* If a process has been improved, employees will typically know about it, especially if they are responsible for implementing the change. Speak to employees in the work area and see if they're familiar with changes and their roles in implementation.

- *Are products/outcomes improved?* This is the essential point: Have the products been improved? An improved process should ultimately lead to improved products. Is there evidence that this has happened? What do records indicate?

- *Has measurement or monitoring been established?* The effectiveness of some corrective action can't be known without ongoing measurement or monitoring of the process. In these cases, have the controls been put in place? What do the measurements indicate? Does the data indicate the process has improved and stabilized to the new level?

- *Has the problem reoccurred?* If the problem continues to reoccur at the same level as before, the corrective action is not effective.

- *Is top management aware of the corrective action?* Top management isn't expected to be aware of every corrective action in the organization, but they should be aware of the large ones and overall trends. Top management awareness would certainly help support a determination of full implementation and communication.

7. HOW IS CUSTOMER FEEDBACK USED?

This question will probably not apply to all personnel. It is especially relevant to top management and those persons tasked with gauging customer perceptions. The question is significant because most organizations do a fair job at capturing perceptions, but a much worse job of doing something with the information. ISO 9001 specifically requires the organization to define methods for obtaining and using data on customer satisfaction. This is a compelling reason for using simple methods for capturing customer perceptions. The more complex and resource intensive your customer satisfaction methods are, the less likely you are to act on what you learn. It's a curious paradox. The reason is that many organizations "run out of gas" before they get to the action phase, and the valuable opportunities afforded by customer feedback fade into obscurity.

It's important to realize that creating pretty charts and graphs is not the point of customer feedback. The point is acting to improve. If we fail to act on feedback, we're fooling ourselves and (even worse) fooling our customers.

8. HOW ARE CUSTOMER COMPLAINTS HANDLED?

Despite everyone's best efforts, customers will occasionally complain. Customer complaints represent both a huge risk and valuable opportunity to the organization—it all depends on how the complaints are handled. This question is especially relevant to sales people, customer service representatives, technical personnel, and top management. The auditor is looking for proof of a systematic approach to dealing with complaints. This typically will include defined responsibilities for logging and tracking complaints, clear problem statements with all relevant facts included, logical analysis of problem causes, and actions taken, as appropriate. Specific examples of complaints will need to be sampled, of course. The linkage between the complaint process and the corrective action process requires special scrutiny. Trends in customer complaints should always trigger corrective action.

When auditing customer complaints, pay special attention to the following:

- *How complaints are received and recorded.* There should be a formal process for handling complaints. The people involved in the process should understand how it works and provide evidence of its functioning.
- *What actions are taken.* Not all customer complaints receive formal action. The auditor should probe when action is taken and who is responsible for carrying it out.
- *Analysis of trends.* Finally, there should be a process in place for analyzing trends in complaints. Trends in customer complaints would, of course, lead to formal corrective action.

9. HOW DOES TOP MANAGEMENT REVIEW THE ORGANIZATION'S PERFORMANCE?

This question relates directly to top management. One of the most important responsibilities of top management is reviewing the organization's performance. I'm not talking about the performance of individuals, of course, but the performance of the organization as a whole. Is your organization becoming more efficient, more competitive, and better at serving customers? Or is it moving in the opposite direction? Top management should regularly analyze data and trends that provide the answers to these questions.

ISO 9001 specifically requires management review, with defined inputs and outputs. There's no sense in conducting an ISO 9001 management review, then conducting a separate review of the organization's performance. They should be the same review. The timelier and action-oriented, the better. Some of the best approaches to reviewing organizational performance are the most creative. Many organizations design their reviews across many different forums and time frames, which is a practical and realistic way to approach the process. Regardless of how the review is configured, the three imperatives include analysis of data, identification of opportunities, and action that is taken on the opportunities. Smart organizations treat these three activities as inseparable.

Special angles of inquiry include:
- What is the specified frequency of management review?
- Who are the participants?
- Have all required inputs been addressed?

- Have all the required outputs been produced?
- Are records complete?
- What are the results of management review? What sort of improvements are triggered by it?
- Is top management personally involved?

10. WHAT EVIDENCE DO YOU HAVE OF CONTINUAL IMPROVEMENT?

This question can be asked of everybody in the organization. In organizations that have communicated the tools of improvement and provided opportunities for their application, this is an easy question. In organizations where improvement efforts are very narrowly applied, it becomes a much harder question. There should certainly be some evidence of continual improvement within the scope of the audit. Strategic improvements are impressive, of course, but all improvements have value. This question summarizes many of the earlier questions into a single point of inquiry. The ultimate purpose of a management system is to provide a means for improvement to take place.

Just because one or two people aren't able to provide evidence of improvement isn't necessarily a problem. It could be an indicator of weak improvement efforts, though. Further investigation would certainly be warranted. In very mature organizations, all personnel are involved in making improvements and proof of this happening is abundant.

Here are some related questions:
- Who is involved in improvement efforts?
- What tools are used in the pursuit of continual improvement?
- How are personnel trained in the use of improvement tools?
- How are improvement ideas prioritized?
- How are employees made aware of improvement efforts and successes?

11. HOW IS TRAINING CARRIED OUT?

This may seem like a strange question to appear on anyone's list of most important audit questions. It's very significant, though. The development of human resources is one of the keys to organizational success. This audit question attempts to probe the work that goes into developing these resources. Is training performed as a knee-jerk activity without any underlying objectives? Or is training geared toward empowering each employee with the skills and knowledge needed to propel the organization forward? This is one of the most significant topics an audit can probe.

Here are specific angles to focus on:

- *Competency requirements.* Competency is the mix of education, training, skills, and experience needed to perform a particular job. The competency requirements should be established for all personnel and used as the basis for training.
- *Orientation training.* Orientation training is not a requirement of ISO 9001, but many organizations do require it. If the organization has committed to using it, make sure it is happening and is supported by records.
- *On the job training.* On the job training, also known as OJT, is one of the oldest and most effective means for training employees. Unfortunately, most organizations approach on the job training in an unstructured way. If the organization uses on the job training, verify that it is happening and that the desired outcomes are achieved.
- *Recurring training.* Some types of training, especially those related to safety and health, happen on a recurring basis. If the organization is doing this type of training, make sure that all applicable personnel are receiving it at the appropriate frequency.
- *Records.* Training and records go hand in hand. In fact, we can confidently say that there is no proof of training unless records clearly support it.
- *Effectiveness.* ISO 9001 requires that the effectiveness of all training be evaluated. There are different ways to do this, ranging from written tests to demonstrations of skills. However the organization elects to do this, make sure it is happening and that it is supported by records.

During the audit, make sure that competency needs have been determined and training has been carried out for all levels of employees, including:

- Top management
- Temporary employees
- Contract personnel

- Technical employees
- Long-term employees
- Recent hires

Training applies to all personnel not just a narrow slice of the organization. Some of the more neglected employee categories from a training perspective have the most impact on organizational success. This is especially true of top management. If you can't remember seeing top management at any training events, then this is ripe fruit for picking.

12. WHAT'S THE MOST IMPORTANT THING ABOUT YOUR JOB?

This is an exploratory question that can take you in valuable directions. The answer to this question can be compared to the formal controls in place (e.g., documentation, training, verifications, data analysis, etc.) to determine how deliberately the management system was designed and implemented. If you learn that the most important thing about the job is receiving timely and complete feedback from the downstream department, then it will be revealing to explore if the feedback exists and what is done with it. This question requires some discretion on the part of the auditor, because the information may or may not lead to any logical conclusions. The auditor must have the experience and maturity to know when he or she has an issue that is worth exploring in detail. In other words, don't allow this question to become an endless fishing expedition. Explore the essential elements of a job, compare what you learn to the controls in place, and cross check the facts with other personnel doing similar jobs. It can produce powerful insights.

There are many other exploratory questions that can also provide some valuable trails for deeper inquiry. These include:

- What's the hardest thing about your job?
- What are some things you'd like to change about your job?
- What is a resource that would help you be more effective?
- What should your manager know that he or she currently doesn't know?
- If you were the manager here, what would you do differently?

The previous 12 questions are timeless quality management system (QMS) topics that could be used in any audit. But what about the new topics that were introduced in ISO 9001:2015? Topics like context, risk, and change management can be challenging to auditors, even ones with considerable experience. Here are a few more audit questions that probe the new requirements of ISO 9001:2015.

13. WHAT CAN YOU TELL ME ABOUT THE CONTEXT OF YOUR ORGANIZATION?

This question is the starting point of ISO 9001:2015, appearing in section 4.1. The standard uses the clunky term "context," but this could easily be substituted by asking about the organization's internal and external success factors. Questions about context are usually directed at top management or the person leading the QMS (formerly known as the management representative).

As an auditor, you're looking for a clear examination of forces at work within and around the organization. Does this sound broad and a little vague? It is. Thankfully, the standard provides some guidance, saying that context must include internal and external issues that are relevant to your organization's purpose, strategy, and the goals of the QMS. Many organizations will probably use SWOT analysis (strengths, weaknesses, opportunities, and threats) to help get their arms around context, but it's not a requirement. What the organization learns with this will be a key input to risk analysis. (NOTE: Not everybody will understand the term "context." Be prepared to discuss the concept and describe what ISO 9001:2015 is asking for.)

14. WHO ARE YOUR INTERESTED PARTIES AND WHAT ARE THEIR REQUIREMENTS?

The natural follow-up to "context" is "interested parties," found in section 4.2. The term "interested parties" has a bizarre, stalker-like ring to it, so smart auditors might want to replace it with "stakeholders." Remember, effective auditors try to translate the arcane language of ISO 9001:2015 into understandable terms that auditees can grasp. Typical interested parties are employees, customers, suppliers, business owners, debt holders, neighbors, and regulators. As an auditor, you're making sure that a reasonable range of interested parties has been identified, along with their corresponding requirements.

The best way to audit interested parties is as an exploratory discussion. Ask questions about the interested parties, and probe what they're interested in. If you've done some preparation in advance of the audit, you'll know whether their examination of interested parties is adequate. That brings up an important planning issue: You will have to do a bit more preparation before an ISO 9001:2015 audit so you'll have a grasp of context and interested parties. How can you evaluate their responses if you don't know what the responses should be?

15. WHAT RISKS AND OPPORTUNITIES HAVE BEEN IDENTIFIED, AND WHAT ARE YOU DOING ABOUT THEM?

Risks and opportunities could accurately be called the foundation of ISO 9001:2015. At least 13 other clauses refer directly to risks and opportunities, making them the most "connected" section of the standard. If an organization does a poor job of identifying risks and opportunities, the QMS cannot be effective. Auditors should verify that risks and opportunities include issues that focus on desired outcomes, prevent problems, and drive improvement. Once risks and opportunities are identified, actions must be planned to address them. ISO 9001:2015 does not specifically mention prioritizing risks and opportunities, though it would be wise for organizations to do this. Risks and opportunities are limitless, but resources are not.

16. WHAT PLANS HAVE BEEN PUT IN PLACE TO ACHIEVE QUALITY OBJECTIVES?

Measurable quality objectives have long been a part of ISO 9001. What is new is the requirement to plan actions to make them happen. The plans are intended to be specific and actionable, addressing actions, resources, responsibilities, timeframes, and evaluation of results. Auditors should closely examine how the organization has implemented plans and who has knowledge of them. Just as employees should be aware of how they contribute to objectives, they should be familiar with the action plans.

17. HOW HAS THE QMS BEEN INTEGRATED INTO THE ORGANIZATION'S BUSINESS PROCESSES?

In other words, how are you using ISO 9001:2015 to help you run the company? This is asked directly of top management (see section 5.1.1c) and is a very revealing question. The point is that ISO 9001 is moving away from being a QMS standard and becoming a strategic management system. It's not just about making sure products or services meet requirements anymore. The standard is about managing every aspect of the business. Remember sections 4.1 and 4.2 of ISO 9001:2015? There we examined the key topics of context and interested parties. These concepts touch every corner of the organization, and this is exactly how ISO 9001:2015 is intended to be used. Top management should be able to describe how the QMS is used to run the company, not just pass an audit.

18. HOW DO YOU MANAGE CHANGE?

This topic comes up multiple times in ISO 9001:2015. The first and biggest clause on the topic comes up in section 6.3. Here we identify changes we know are coming and develop plans for their implementation. What kind of changes? Nearly anything, but the following changes come to mind as candidates: new or modified products, processes, equipment, tools, employees, regulations. The list is endless. An auditor should review changes that took place and seek evidence that the change was identified and planned proactively. Change that happens in a less planned manner is addressed in section 8.5.6. Here the auditor will seek records that the changes met requirements, the results of reviewing changes, who authorized them, and subsequent actions that were necessary.

19. HOW DO YOU CAPTURE AND USE KNOWLEDGE?

ISO 9001:2015 wants organizations to learn from their experiences, both good and bad. This could be handled by a variety of means: project debriefs, job close-outs, staff meetings, customer reviews, examination of data, customer feedback. How the organization captures knowledge is up to it, but the process should be clear and functional. The knowledge should also be maintained and accessible. This almost sounds like it will be "documented" in some way, doesn't it? That's exactly right. One way to audit this would be to inquire about recent failures or successes. How did the organization learn from these events in a way that will help make them more successful? It's the conversion of raw information to true knowledge, and it just happens to be one of the most difficult things an organization can achieve.

Here's a final thought: The most important audit questions ultimately depend on the organization. The questions presented only represent a slice of what might matter to a typical organization. You will need to tweak and refine this list, based on the special concerns and risks faced by your company. Figure out what matters most to your organization and focus your audit process on those things. There isn't enough time and energy to focus on everything. An audit process that keeps its eyes on the organization's key success factors will always be relevant and always produce powerful results.

Chapter 17

Audit Practice

The ability to analyze an audit situation and write findings is a fundamental audit competency. The only way you become skillful in these tasks is through a lot of practice. That's the purpose of this chapter: to give you some practice from the comfort of your own office. The good news is that actual auditing with real people is immensely easier than auditing against a case situation. If you can audit these situations, real auditing will be a walk in the park.

Read each situation below, identifying what appears to be the key issues. Then find the applicable company document at the end of the situations. It should be relatively clear which of the documents apply. Write the nonconformities that apply to each situation. Include all identifiers and traceable details, and make sure to write in complete sentences. The correct answers are shown at the end of the chapter.

SITUATION 1 (WRITE 2 NONCONFORMITIES)

One of the auditors accompanied the quality manager into his office to talk about his role in the quality management system. The auditor asked which parts of the system he was responsible for. "Well, internal audits, corrective action, management review, quality objectives, and risks and opportunities," the quality manager said.

The auditor nodded. "How do you keep up with risks and opportunities?" the auditor asked.

The quality manager pulled out a large spreadsheet and showed it to the auditor. "We get the management team together and brainstorm the issues," he said. "Last month we compiled over 100 risks."

The auditor examined the spreadsheet, taking note of the many risks that had been identified and their associated actions. "You and your team did a nice job with this," the auditor said.

The quality manager nodded and said thanks.

"Who was involved with the analysis of risks and opportunities?" the auditor continued.

The quality manager pointed to the spreadsheet and said, "It was me, the general manager, and the VP of operations."

The auditor examined the spreadsheet and saw the names of participants. "How about the inputs to the process of risks and opportunities," he said. "Did you make use of the context of the organization or interested parties when you examined risks?"

The quality manager took the spreadsheet back from the auditor. "We view the analysis of risks and opportunities as one of the most important processes in our QMS, so we started with that. It's part of our strategic planning process. I figure we'll look at context of the organization and interested parties in the next few weeks. We started with the important things first."

Requirement:

_____

_____

_____

_____

Finding:

_____

_____

_____

_____

Requirement:

_____

_____

_____

_____

Finding:

_____

_____

_____

_____

SITUATION 2 (WRITE 2 NONCONFORMITIES)

An auditor asked one of the finishing associates how his day was going. The associate replied, "Fine. This is an excellent batch of flanges. I'm getting them packaged and ready to ship. It's order No. 11436 for ACME Machining of Chula Vista."

The auditor nodded as he watched the packaging process. "Do you have any guidelines for packaging?" the auditor asked.

The associate nodded and showed the auditor a packaging specification. "This is a 971 flange," the associate said. "As you can see, the specification addresses all the packaging requirements."

The auditor examined the specification. "Yes, it's very detailed."

The associate continued packaging the flanges, which involved wrapping each one in flexible plastic film, and then placing them in a 12″ × 12″ × 24″ cardboard box. "Each flange is actually composed of two pieces, a top half and a bottom half. I put all the top halves in one box and all bottom halves in a separate box, because they'll get scratched if I pack them together," the associate said.

"What kind of labeling and paperwork is required?" the auditor asked.

The associate showed the auditor a packing list that had been inserted in a box. "The only thing needed is a packing list. After the box is sealed, it will get a shipping label with the ship-to address on it."

Requirement:

_____
_____
_____
_____

Finding:

_____
_____
_____
_____

Requirement:

_____
_____
_____
_____

Finding:

_____
_____
_____
_____

SITUATION 3 (WRITE 1 NONCONFORMITY)

The auditor toured plant No. 1. He found a pallet of A-31 steel blanks that were standing in an aisle next to an operator desk. The auditor stopped and asked about the pallet.

"I noticed this pallet is outside the normal production flow," the auditor said. "Is there anything special about it?"

The department manager nodded his head and said, "Yes, as a matter of fact, there is. The pallet is on hold because the steel blanks are too narrow."

The auditor examined the pallet, and he didn't see any kind of special labeling on it. "I don't see any kind of 'on hold' labeling on it. How is the product identified as being nonconforming?"

The department manager pointed to a pallet label that included a bar code. "If you scan that bar code," the department manager said, "our production system will show you it's on hold." The manager scanned the pallet label with a bar code gun, and the computer screen showed that the pallet was nonconforming.

The auditor examined the screen and nodded. "What would happen if someone tried to use or move the pallet?" the auditor asked.

The department manager said, "The production system wouldn't let them. You have to scan the pallet label at every production step, and it clearly indicates that the pallet is on hold and not to be used."

The auditor smiled. "It sounds like a good system," the auditor said.

The department manager agreed and said, "Thank you. It seems to work very well for us."

Requirement:

_____

_____

_____

_____

Finding:

_____

_____

_____

_____

SITUATION 4 (WRITE 2 NONCONFORMITIES)

The auditor entered the final inspection area where a quality assurance technician was visually inspecting a chrome handle.

"That's a very handsome handle," the auditor said, noting the highly reflective finish. "What do you look for when you inspect the parts?"

The technician showed a handle to the auditor. "There are a few things we're looking for," the technician said. "The first thing is any kind of smudges, dust, or oil. I can wipe those off without any problems. Then I look for scratches that are longer than 8 millimeters. These can't be fixed and any handles having them must be put on hold and reworked. I also looked for burs or rough edges on the back side of the handles, and any sort of off-color in the chrome plating. Sometimes there might be some yellowing. As you can see, the inspection criterion is very simple, so we don't need any kind of written specification."

The auditor nodded. "How is this lot of handles looking?" the auditor asked.

The technician smiled and said, "It's looking very good so far. I haven't had to put anything on hold."

The auditor examined one the handles. "How about measuring instruments. Do you use any measuring instruments during your inspection process?"

The technician shook his head and said, "No, it's entirely visual. I just write the inspection results on the work order, and the finishing department takes it from there."

Requirement:

_____

_____

_____

_____

Finding:

_____

_____

_____

_____

Requirement:

_____

_____

_____

_____

Finding:

_____

_____

_____

_____

Control of Nonconforming Products Procedure

Doc. No. OP-015, Revision 3

Approved by: Craig Cochran

1. Nonconforming products are removed from the regular production flow.
2. Information on nonconforming products is entered into the production system using a bar code. The production system prevents nonconforming products from being used or moved.
3. Nonconforming products may also be labeled in with a red HOLD tag. In the event that a red HOLD tag is not used, the nonconforming products must be segregated in the locked nonconforming cage.
4. Disposition of nonconforming products will be performed by the quality manager and are entered into the production system.
5. If the disposition is "Return to Vendor," the purchasing manager will send a Return Material Authorization form to the receiving manager along with the Material Discrepancy Report. Both of these will accompany the product when it is sent to the supplier.
6. Records of nonconforming products and their dispositions are maintained per the records procedure.
7. Trends in nonconforming products will be monitored. Corrective action will be taken on trends as deemed appropriate by management.

Visual Inspection Procedure

Doc. No. OP-009, Revision 3

Approved by: Craig Cochran

1. All chromed or plated products must receive visual inspection prior to finishing.
2. Visual inspectors must have at least 30 days of on-the-job training working with an experienced inspector.
3. Visual inspection should take place within 24 hours of being chromed.
4. Finishing department personnel must confirm inspection results on the work order prior to packaging.
5. A written product specification must be present during all inspection activities.

6. Any measurements must be performed using calibrated measuring instruments. Prior to being used, technicians must confirm the gauge's status through its calibration label.
7. Any products with visual defects are subject to the Control of Nonconforming Products procedure.

971 FLANGE Packaging Specification

Doc. No. XXX-971, Revision 2
Approved by: Craig Cochran

1. All flanges must receive dimensional and visual inspection prior to packaging.
2. All flanges must be wrapped in flexible plastic wrap.
3. Flanges must be packed in 12" × 12" × 24" cardboard boxes.
4. The top and bottom halves of all flanges must be packaged in the same box.
5. Packing lists must be generated and inserted in each box prior to sealing.
6. A Certificate of Analysis, showing all test results, must be printed and accompany the shipment.
7. A shipping label must be clearly affixed to the top of each cardboard box after being sealed.

Risks and Opportunities Procedure

Doc. No. OP-033, Revision 0
Approved by: Craig Cochran

1. Risks and opportunities will be updated on an annual basis during the strategic planning cycle. This typically takes place in September or October of each year, though alternate timeframes may be utilized at the discretion of top management.
2. Brainstorming will be used to identify potential risks and opportunities. A facilitator is recommended to assist in the process. When determining risks and opportunities, context of the organization and interested parties must be considered as inputs to the process.
3. Risks will be identified through a discovery process, utilizing customer complaints, internal nonconformities, safety near misses, audit findings,

and/or other inputs. Opportunities will be identified in a similar manner, utilizing marketing forecasts, customer feedback, design requests, competitor analyses, and/or other inputs.

4. Risks are prioritized by the management team. Risks determined to have higher significance are addressed with action plans. Each plan must include actions to be taken, resources needed, responsibilities, and timeframes.

5. The following personnel must be involved in the identification or updating of risks and opportunities (and associated actions): CEO, VP of sales, VP of operations, general manager, and quality manager.

6. The records from risks and opportunities must be saved on the Q drive in the folder labeled "RISKS."

ANSWERS

Your nonconformity statements do not need to be identical to these, as there are many different ways to write-up the same situation. They should be very similar, though, and include all the same identifiers.

Situation 1

Nonconformity 1

- Requirement: The Risks and Opportunities Procedure (Doc. No. OP-033, Revision 0) states in section 2, "When determining risks and opportunities, context of the organization and interested parties must be considered as inputs to the process."
- Finding: The quality manager stated that risks and opportunities had been determined without considering the context of the organization and interested parties.

Nonconformity 2

- Requirement: The Risks and Opportunities Procedure (Doc. No. OP-033, revision 0) states in section 5, "The following personnel must be involved in the identification or updating of risks and opportunities (and associated actions): CEO, VP of Sales, VP of operations, general manager, and quality manager."

- Finding: The spreadsheet of risks and opportunities indicated that the quality manager, general manager, and the VP of operations were involved in the most recent identification of risks and opportunities. The CEO and VP of sales were not involved.

Situation 2

Nonconformity 1

- Requirement: The 971 Flange Packaging Specification (Doc. No. XXX-971, revision 2) states in section 4, "The top and bottom halves of all flanges must be packaged in the same box."
- Finding: A finishing associate who was packing 971 flanges (order 11436 for ACME Machining of Chula Vista) stated that he packed all the top halves in one box and all bottom halves in a separate box because they would get scratched if he packed them together.

Nonconformity 2

- Requirement: The 971 Flange Packaging Specification (Doc. No. XXX-971, revision 2) states in section 6, "A Certificate of Analysis, showing all test results, must be printed and accompany the shipment."
- Finding: The finishing associate packing an order of 971 flanges (order No. 11436 for ACME Machining of Chula Vista) stated that the only paperwork needed was a packing list. The auditor observed that only a packing list was inserted into the box of 971 flanges.

Situation 3

Nonconformity 1

- Requirement: The Control of Nonconforming Products Procedure (Doc. No. OP-015, revision 3) states in section 3, "Nonconforming products may also be labeled with a red HOLD tag. In the event that a red HOLD tag is not used, the nonconforming products must be segregated in the locked nonconforming cage."

- Finding: The auditor observed a pallet of A-31 steel blanks that were standing in an aisle next to an operator desk. The pallet was nonconforming, but a red HOLD tag had not been used for identification, nor had the pallet been segregated in the locked nonconforming cage.

Situation 4

Nonconformity 1

- Requirement: The Visual Inspection Procedure (Doc. No. OP-009, revision 3) states in section 5, "A written product specification must be present during all inspection activities."
- Finding: A QA technician in the final inspection area was visually inspecting chrome handles. He stated that the inspection criteria were very simple, so he didn't need any sort of written specification.

Nonconformity 2

- Requirement: The Visual Inspection Procedure (Doc. No. OP-009, revision 3) states in section 6, "Any measurements must be performed using calibrated measuring instruments. Prior to being used, technicians must confirm the gauge's status through its calibration label."
- Finding: A QA technician in the final inspection area was visually inspecting chrome handles. The inspection criteria include scratches that are longer than 8 millimeters, but calibrated measuring instruments are not used to verify the length of scratches.

Chapter 18

Conclusion

E ven the best book is little more than a series of clever words. To convert these words to knowledge, they must be combined with a lot of practice and real-life experience. That's your assignment now: Go out and get as much experience auditing as you can. Do everything you can to refine your auditing skills and be recognized for them. Auditing is a continual journey of skill building. You will never reach a point when you can say, "I've learned everything I can about auditing." You're fooling yourself if you ever think that. Here are steps you can take to stay in a state of learning on auditing:

- *Network with other auditors.* Trade stories, successes, and failures. You can learn a great deal about auditing simply by hearing the experiences of those who are working in the trenches.
- *Audit as often as possible.* The more you do it, the more comfortable you will be and the sharper your skills will become. Make sure to spread your time across all phases of the audit process, including planning, preparation, evidence gathering, drawing conclusions, and reporting.
- *Read about auditing.* Try to stay current with auditing through articles, posts, and other forms of writing. Nuggets of wisdom and best practices can be found here, and they can be put to work immediately.
- *Write about auditing.* As your experience and knowledge in auditing grows, you will undoubtedly feel the need to share this with others. Begin scribbling down your thoughts on auditing as they pop into your head. A few sentences can turn into a few paragraphs, and this can turn into a

blog post or article. Who knows? You might even write your own book on auditing in one day.

- *Audit a wide variety of organizations.* Seek opportunities for auditing new and unusual organizations, including nonprofits, governmental entities, sole proprietorships, large international companies, service firms, manufacturers, laboratories, warehouses and logistics centers, and anything else you can find.

- *Audit against a variety of standards.* Most auditors have a standard or two that they're comfortable auditing, but others that they would prefer to avoid. Truly skilled auditors seize the opportunity to audit against different standards because they provide valuable perspectives and alternative requirements that add to the auditor's competency. You can use what you learn auditing against an environmental standard during an ISO 9001 audit, for instance. The more experience you have with different standards, the more versatile a thinker you'll be during an audit.

- *Get certified.* Numerous certifications exist through organizations like the American Society for Quality, Exemplar Global (formerly RABQSA), and others. These certifications generally include some sort of competency examination in addition to education, work experience, and auditing experience. They are worthwhile ways for auditors to receive outside recognition for their auditing knowledge and abilities.

- *Mentor new auditors.* Everybody needs and appreciates mentors, especially new auditors. Offer to fill this role by guiding and assisting new auditors in developing their potential. It will provide great value to others, and you'll find that your own auditing will improve as you strive to be a positive example. Another benefit of being around new auditor is that they will end up teaching *you.* New auditors often approach the auditing process in novel and unique ways, and these unusual approaches can prove very helpful.

- *Remember the principles of auditing.* Primarily, you're not just hunting for nonconformities. You're taking an unbiased and balanced snapshot of the organization, both positives and negatives. Remember that the ideal mindset of an auditor is a learning mindset. As an auditor, you're looking forward to having friendly conversations with fascinating people. Your goal is to establish a partnership of improvement with the auditee.

Thank for you including this book on your auditing journey. I hope you spend many happy years helping organizations become more successful.

Printed in Great Britain
by Amazon

81516118R00102